the
Other Side
of God

The Eleven Gem Odyssey of Being

Susan D. Kalior
M. A. in Education in Counseling
Human Relations and Behavior
B.S. in Sociology

Blue Wing Publications, Workshops, and Lectures
Tualatin, Oregon

The Other Side of God:
The Eleven Gem Odyssey of Being
Copyright©2007 by Susan D Kalior
First Printing: May 2007
ISBN 978-0-9795663-0-1

Published by Blue Wing Publications, Workshops, and Lectures
Cover Design by Laura C. Keyser
Logo by Sara C. Roethle
Author Photo by Stephen Roethle

Blue Wing Publications, Workshops, and Lectures
P.O. Box 947, Tualatin, OR 97062
sdk@bluewingworkshops.com
www. bluewingworkshops.com
Readers' comments are welcomed.

Other Books by Susan D. Kalior

The Other Side of Life: The Eleven Gem Odyssey of Death

Warriors in the Mist: A Medieval Dark Fantasy

Growing Wings Self Discovery Workbook:
17 Workshops to a Better Life

Johnny, the Mark of Chaos: An Urban Dark Fantasy

Jenséa, an Angel's Touch: Into the World of Johnny

Manufactured in the United States of America

Dedication

*This book is dedicated
in loving memory
to my wonderful mother
Carole Lee Kalior
who left her body
Nov 28, 2005.
May her spirit soar.*

Acknowledgements

Special thanks to my devoted and loving sister, Cindy Kalior, whose enthusiasm and respect for my work gives me great courage. Thanks to my brother, Mark Kalior, for his wizardly insights and scientific advice. Thank you to my father who coached me in the art of handling adversity, and to my nurturing mother who placed her heart in mine. Thank you to Sara C. Roethle, Matthew A. Keyser, and Laura Keyser, for their extensive time and effort aiding in proofreading. Thanks to Laura also for serving as my Grammarian, and book cover artist. Thank you to Stephen Roethle, and Jennifer Kalior for so lovingly supporting my endeavor. Particular thanks, with deep respect to "My Fool on the Hill."

Prologue

He'd always known more than most, oh not like E=Mc squared, or how to fix a broken car, or even the alphabet. No. He knew things like how to get a high school diploma without going to high school, how to choose a woman He'd never met to be His wife and thirty days later marry her, and how to become a self-made millionaire before age forty.

He knew the law of the jungle, the power of bluff, and how to make dreams come true. He knew how to wear masks and how to make money. He knew airports, hotels, liquor, the high of victory and the low of a family falling apart. Alas, He knew that He must retreat from the fast lane to the back alley, and travel the rough-shod road of His heart into something deeper still. You see . . . He knew a lot.

When His ambition changed from conquering the world to conquering Himself, a miraculous thing occurred. He journeyed within and became a great explorer of unseen realms, questing the riches of wisdom, the secrets to holistic existence, and communion with the quintessential life force.

One cannot enter the inner realm when guided by beliefs acquired from living in the outer world, for every step taken leads out—not in. So, He discarded perceived notions of reality, crossed deserts of loneliness, and became stuck in mud lakes that held Him immobile for months. And, no matter where He went, He always felt lost.

He encountered a red-eyed power monger, a deserted child, and a mysterious woman whose touch frightened Him. He wanted to run back to the familiar outside world and call His experience fantasy, but the brilliance of His quest paled surface existence.

He could *almost* feel the face of His true self, *almost* taste freedom, *almost* see unimaginable beauty invisible to the human eye.

So, like all great explorers, He did not give up.

1

He discovered symphonies that bespoke wisdom. He slipped into the essence of tree, rock, bird, and squirrel—even snakes, even toads. He found that getting everything required giving everything, and that sometimes losing was really winning, and that getting somewhere meant going nowhere. He grew wings to fly in the skies of the mind, and gills to swim in the depths of the unconscious, and eyes that could see into the dark unknown.

I too, trek the unseen world. I would see Him now and again, with glowing body and mystical eyes, smiling. Not the brand of smile born from a joke. No. His smile held the world, and His glittering eyes, the Universe. He climbed life's gargantuan mountain, a switch back or two ahead of me. Behind Him, moist fog hugged solid rock, concealing jagged edges, protrusions, and crags that cut, imbalance, and make one fall. Now and then, from those rocky cliffs above, He would toss a gem of brilliant wisdom into my knapsack.

Each gem gave me a flash of clarity. And opposites became the same. Solid was fluid, leaving—coming, in—out, and the center—whole. These insights echo through me with an ancient knowing that wakes me from this dream called Life. It is my job to translate these insights to the human ear. But even more, it is my job to beckon you enter this incredible place where even the sky is not the limit.

This book is the map, and the pages—the journey. Not His . . . yours. Each sentence will lead you deeper into yourself, beyond perceived reality into unknown regions that will broaden your definition of life. To begin, you must cross the State Line. Crossing the State Line means stepping beyond the walls of thought that cement your reality.

Be present now, if you choose to turn this page, for this is a journey from which you will never return. Never. Returning would be like walking in a reflection, away from the core that nourishes your soul. This journey has no end, because it leads into the moment, which is eternal.

Now, take a step. Come inside yourself. Enter the unseen world. Come. It is time to experience "illumination and joy."

Crossing the State Line

"You get what you see, you see what you get."

GEM #1 PERCEPTION

I crossed the State Line, entering the bountiful Universe within, seeking a sage of unseen worlds known as The Fool on the Hill. There I stood in a desert bright, lively with groundhog and bird, cacti plump and prickly pear abundant.

My Fool was there, as if waiting for me. I shook my head and blinked. His face seemed like the moon, His eyes like whirling saucers. I half expected His voice to sound like thunder, or a saxophone, or the sound of one hand clapping; however, His tone was normal like any other, as if He were no big deal, as if life were no big deal.

He said, "Welcome to the *real* world, Susan."

Was my world not real?

I raised my brows and peeked over my shoulder, gazing into the mundane world from whence I came. I viewed a mirror that had no beginning, nor end—this mirror that reflected the outer world. My image was simple: a five foot two female, long brown hair, and hazel eyes—adventure bound in my long-sleeved, navy-blue tee shirt and jeans, brown hiking boots, and russet knapsack slung over my right shoulder. Just a woman. Just a simple ordinary woman.

His voice flowed low behind me, then inside me. "Peer beyond the image. What do you see?"

I stared into my face. "A wife, mother of two, psychotherapist, writer, and humanitarian."

"Look deeper still. What do you see?"

"A seeker . . . of—myself."

From behind me, I felt him smile—a smile so gentle, it roared in my heart.

"Bravo," He said. "If you dare see more, turn *away* from the mirror, away from the outer world reflection."

I turned away from the mirror. Facing Him, I gulped. I didn't mean to gulp. It just came out.

"You can return to the mirror if you choose."

I shook my head vigorously. "No, I can't." I bowed my head inadvertently staring at my heart. "I'm losing myself," I glanced at the mirror, "out there."

He stood before me. His body seemed like liquid energy, clear steam, not as solid as mine, for My Fool on the Hill dwelled in the half world between the corporeal and other side of life, what many call death.

His whimsical eyes penetrated deep into the ailing part of me, like a daddy tickling His child, saying, 'ah, there's much to smile about.'

"I am ready," I said, "I must do this."

He nodded. "Very well then. Your odyssey begins."

Now that I had passed the 'cold feet' stage, My Fool appeared less mysterious: short gray hair, mustache, and a well-kept beard. A violet sweatshirt and white pants clothed His sturdy body, a few inches taller than mine. Headphones hugged His ears, and an outdated Sony Walkman His waist.

He whistled casually, relaxed stance, wearing jogging shoes with the toe part cut out. I'd ask Him about that later. First things first.

I pointed to His Walkman. "What's playing?"

His whistle turned to words, but the rhythm seemed the same. "Gustav Mahler's *Symphony No.3,* the first movement." His eyes closed.

It seemed like He'd left me. I waited.

Finally, with an ecstatic sigh, His eyes opened, whirling again. "Have you beheld the works of the symphonic composer, Gustav Mahler?"

I shook my head. "No, but I'd like to."

He peered into me. "Would you?"

I felt strange for a second, but then nodded lightly.

"The vibration of this music stimulates the mystically abstract arenas of my psyche to serve as sort of a . . . flying carpet into unseen worlds." His hands cupped the headphones. "This music flies me into expanded awareness."

His eyelids started to close, but then one rose brusquely and a wizardly eye targeted me. A flash of light shot into my forehead, exploding starburst glimmers, migraine headache style.

The impact dizzied me. "What's it like," I shook my head lightly to make the dizziness go away, "in expanded awareness?"

"I experience pure, unfiltered, shapeless, boundless, timeless, all embracing—energy."

I listened intently.

"But then something happens."

"What, what happens?"

"Words aren't sufficient, but I shall endeavor to explain. It is as if this pure energy, transcendent of time and space, wants to know itself. Its *self* is—*all that is*, without separate parts; therefore, to facilitate exploration, it generates the concept of time, space, and matter, with the *impression* of separation. Energy rays, or what one might call 'beings,' journey forth to have various adventures of, 'What would happen if . . . ?' "

His words became a bit faint when a visiting buzzing bee hovered uncomfortably close to my ear. This bee mustn't distract me! I forced myself to focus on My Fool's exciting words.

"The best way I can communicate this awareness, is that these 'beings' emanate into various locations with a forward momentum. They assume identities with individual perceptions of reality. This sets the stage for interaction."

My eyes slid sideways to the bee without losing focus on My Fool. "So then, interacting as separate beings with individual perceptions allows this pure energy to explore itself?"

"Yes. For instance, how do you perceive the bee?"

"I perceive it as a thing that might sting me." I stepped sideways trying to distance myself from the bee, but it remained close, obsessed with my head.

"And the bee might perceive your head as a flower."

I began a little dance to dodge my buzzing foe, but it shadowed me, as bees often do. I almost tripped over a small boulder behind my right ankle, but stopped the fall in an unbecoming clown-like manner. I cleared my throat, embarrassed, and claimed a studious pose, trying to regain my dignity.

He laughed. "This little bee drama exists because you perceive the bee and yourself as separate entities."

I wasn't laughing. The bee was dangerously close to landing on my nose, and so near, I could see the hair on its orange and black body. My eyes crossed. "So, I am *not* separate from this bee?"

"Perceive oneness with the bee and watch what happens."

"All right." My eyes closed in resolute concentration. My head felt like gentle moving waves. *The bee and I are one. The bee is me. I am the bee.* The buzzing diminished. My eyes opened. No bee. "Amazing! I wonder if that works on people."

He chuckled. "You'd be surprised."

"Tell me more of this energy—this oneness."

His voice echoed from inside my mind as if He really were in there. "Visualize this: Your body fades into pure, all-embracing, boundless energy that transcends definition and conscious knowing. Everything you think and feel, everything you *think* you are, is absorbed into this energy. You have transcended time, space, and life as you know it. You experience *all that is* without limits."

My fingers tingled. Electrical sensations charged my body. The top front center of my head almost hurt. Quite suddenly, a mystical feeling overcame me like a cool wave quelling a hot beach. Was this energy—God? I was about to ask My Fool, when He answered. Apparently, He could read my mind.

"Some might call this energy—God, in an attempt to define it, but it is beyond definition, beyond all concepts of God."

"So this energy cannot be defined?"

"Definitions are boxes we put things in to enhance understanding. However, we only see what is in the box. Ironically, definitions can also limit understanding."

"So then, defining can diminish meaning."

"Of course definition is essential to a collective of individuals. Yet, true awareness includes the realization that definition is influenced by perception. Points of view are determined by where one stands in life."

"Yes, our life circumstance would affect our viewpoint."

He swept His hand sideways, palm out, as if opening an invisible curtain. A scene appeared, like a hologram. A notable mountain loomed, peppered with and surrounded by people who spiraled outward beyond my field of vision.

He continued, "Each person perceives the mountain anywhere from a little to a lot different, from bigger to smaller, and maybe from a great distance they might not perceive the mountain at all. Some perceive their view from high on the peak, or low from the base. Some might see an eagle in a nest, ants on a boulder, or just rock. Some might see people hiking on trails, or a tiny mountain in the far distance. From an overview, the mountain might be viewed as a pyramid, or from underground, a solid ceiling. Defining the mountain from every possible angle on earth is ongoing, for the mountain too is ever changing. Agreeing upon one perception is unlikely and can generate argument."

"Yes," I said, "differing views can do that."

He swept His hand back the other way, palm inward, and the scene disappeared. "Hence, the hullabaloo over defining God. Who and what is God? Where is God? Is there more than one—or any? There are many answers. They are all right, and they are all wrong. Or, shall we say, they are not right or wrong. Perceptions bear truth, just not all truth."

I hugged my stomach. "So, defining promotes, yet limits comprehension. Interesting duality. Can we ever see all?"

He reached over and gently unfolded my arms. "Well, there is always more to see. However, it is The Fool's way to ever widen the scope of perception."

My forehead crumpled in deep consternation. "But how can I understand this pure, unfiltered, shapeless, boundless, timeless, all-embracing energy if it can't be defined?"

"Open the skies of your mind and *experience* without trying to *define*. Understand, without knowing. Become, without judgment. You will take your own journey, not mine. You will have insights that needn't comply with the insights of others. It is the way it is supposed to be, the journey of individuality."

"Can we call this energy a name, just between us, so we can communicate?"

"Very well, for this purpose, let us call it—Creative Energy."

"Creative Energy," I mimicked curiously. "If Creative Energy involves this spiritual feeling, then maybe people's effort over the centuries to describe their spiritual experience is what gives root to religion."

"Yes," He said, "religious interpretations are often built on the findings of old writings, versions of old stories, or even unexplainable experiences of a single person. When a group of people accept a text, story, experience, or interpretation as sacred truth, it can indeed become a religion. These shared interpretations, however, are colored by personal experience along with familial and cultural beliefs prevalent in the time and place one lives. Thus, the creation of many religions and versions thereof, provide copious avenues of exploration."

His words evoked a multifaceted crystal in my mind. Each facet reflected a different image of people praying in different ways to different ideas of deity, superimposed by spiritual icons, ancient scrolls, and sacred books.

He smiled at me like He had a front row seat in my mind. "My journey into expanded awareness reveals that religions are based on perceiving mere facets of Creative Energy. Most believe their interpretation is the one and only truth, instead of 'a' truth or 'a' perception among millions. However, conviction to a religious perception can create an intensely powerful sense of community, security, charity, hope, love, and generally draw out what is purest within us. Religious conviction often is a sensing of the mother ship, a remembering that we are somehow connected to something larger. On the flip side, religious perceptions can motivate war, fear, rage, false security, and misinformation. They can aggravate our insecurities, and make us feel inferior to a superior power. Either way, religion is a key theme in the Great Earth Story."

"Story?" I inquired, eyeing a rather large brown snake curled under an overhanging rock, a little too near me. First the bee, and now the snake. I kept seeing things that unnerved me, and *that* unnerved me.

I watched the snake cautiously as He spoke. "Earth is a setting for a great story to unfold, encompassing multiple themes, rich plots, and diverse characters. The concept of religion contributes much. A common scenario is The Good, The Evil, and The Lost. The Good and The Evil lurk on opposite ends of the moral spectrum, perpetuating a battle to sway the in-between Lost to one side or the other. However, just which side is good and which is evil tends to be obscure. The supposed evil, often perceive themselves as holy. And the supposed holy are often perceived as evil. Perceptions. All just—perceptions."

I noticed the snake had uncurled, a python, I thought. Its head lifted our way. Was it looking at us? I wondered if He knew it was there, but on My Fool spoke as if it wasn't, or maybe He just did not care.

"Symbolically speaking, to view the entire crystal of Creative Energy, one must transcend all facets of religious concept into the unedited, unlabeled, undefined whole masterpiece of life."

The idea felt freeing. Oh, how exciting to experience a way of being that encompassed all paths, all ways, yet adhered to none! "So, this journey to find myself is *not* about exploring 'a' philosophy or belief system; it is an unrestricted free flight journey to behold everything, yet cling to no thing."

"Yes. You can see then, the importance of thinking beyond perceptions, terms of religion, and borders of beliefs."

My mouth opened softly. For a moment, I felt 'the beyond.' "It's like, thinking 'inside the box' blinds one from greater beauty."

He adjusted His headphones as if needing to hear the words He was going to say. "Greater beauty, greater wisdom, and a greater sense of 'becoming.' "

"Yes," I said, with my hand pressed over my heart. My chest hurt. Something had been dying inside me for years, squeezed by the python of judgment that sealed me in a box.

Suddenly, the snake disappeared. The inner world must work like that, kind of like dreams.

With head tilted back, He tapped one finger to His chin. "The snake reflected how you constrict yourself. You are beginning to expand, so the snake disappeared."

I had the distinct sense that He knew more about me than I knew about myself.

"Sit." He gestured for me to sit as if there were actually a chair for me to sit upon. However, I saw only dirt and a smattering of weed clumps.

He sat on a seeming invisible chair in a bit of a cocky stance, hands on thighs, elbows out—My Fool.

I thought if I sat, maybe an invisible chair might also support me, but my behind hit the hard ground. Dirt blew up into a powder on my jeans. My face flushed embarrassment, but I feigned inner presence and proceeded to position myself in a half lotus, enjoying the warm earth beneath me. I was such a phony ever pretending I didn't feel what I did, acting like I had all the energy in the world to serve others, when really I was drained dry. Suddenly, I realized how I malnourished myself, deriving worth by being a perfect sacrificial lamb for the greater good. I gasped in realization, "I think like a martyr. That is a box I live in."

He leaned back on His invisible chair and crossed His arms. "When inside the box, the box is not perceived as such, but rather as the environment or reality of the person. One can only recognize his or her box if they transcend it, even . . . if only for a moment. The box, when transcended, appears smaller, despite the familiarity it once brought. The world around seems vaster, livelier, and more colorful."

"It does," I said, "it really does."

He nodded richly. "Congratulations for seeing outside your box."

I wanted badly to release the stronghold of my box, rather than just glimpse what was beyond it from time to time, and His next words felt like super glue dissolvent. "You get what you see and you see what you get. Widen your view and your reality expands. Anything can happen here in the inner world once you cross the State Line—anything. You are in the realm that creates the outer world, where dreams and nightmares are born, sustained, or broken—where you can see the beginnings that gave you today."

His words held power. Like iron granules to a magnet, they fired my heart, making it ache—but a good ache, like stiff muscles, stiff thinking, massaged back to life. I became acutely aware of my boundaries and the large morality I housed within them. This morality had pushed the real me back into the dark and lonely recesses of myself, restricting me to a tiny corner. I had to be good and perfect in accordance to majority view. The real me was a little wisp of a thing crying out, 'Hear me. See me. Touch me.' But I had never listened, seen, nor touched my true self. I thought I had. I was sure of it. But I was wrong. What is *self* anyway?

I pushed down my tears, held my repose, and projected the demure of a duteous pupil. Had to be good, you know, had to be good. I hugged my stomach, feeling bad.

He leaned over and once more gently unfolded my arms. "The idea of good, and for that matter evil, is deeply housed in the perception of deity, and fear of death. These perceptions *reflect* Creative Energy, but do not reveal the *source*."

I leaned forward. "How do we find the source?"

"Shift your focus from outer world reflections, inward to your core being. The core being of one is the core being of all. Within that core, universes are born and creation itself emerges."

I eyed Him studiously. "And then what?"

"Then . . ." He said, "then do that."

"Oh," I exclaimed as if coming awake, "all right."

I closed my eyes and focused on looking to my core being. My head felt strange, like my mind was journeying inward pretty fast into a tunnel.

"Move deeper within, deeper to the source, to the source of all reflection, to the source of all perception."

I jolted. As I traveled through the tunnel I felt something immense and saw something beautiful, but I didn't know what it was, and I couldn't describe it. "I . . . I . . . it's so beautiful."

"Don't define it. Don't put it in a box and assign it a religion. Go deeper Susan, deeper."

I continued the journey, feeling a veil between me and the immense beauty I was moving towards. The veil became dense and deeply gray.

"Keep going," He said.

I cried out in fear, "If I keep going, I might lose myself. I might forget who I am!"

"Or remember," He said.

"I want to remember." A salty tear slipped down my cheek.

"Then forget who you *think* you are, and you will experience who you *really* are. Leave everything behind: your home, children, work, and identity. Move into the beauty, stripped of perceptions, empty like a vase, hollow like a reed. Whatever you leave behind, you will find before you—in its pure state."

I flew beyond the veil reeling into the unknown, tearful at all I left behind and might never see again, despite My Fool's assurance. I began expanding into infinity. I was an energy that overwhelmed me. The beauty . . . the beauty. My body vibrated. The vibrating increased as the beauty, the power intensified. My body couldn't sustain it. I couldn't sustain it. Screams exploded from my mouth, screams of awe, and 'muchness.'

I found myself on the warm desert earth again, flat on my back, breathing heavily, face wet with tears.

My Fool stood over me, smiling gently. Potent wisdom poured through His rich brown eyes that gazed into mine.

"What happened?" My voice was raspy.

"You experienced an inkling of Pure Creative Energy."

"You mean like what people *call* God?"

"No, Susan. Much . . . much more. You experienced the Other Side of God."

"The Other Side of God?"

He adjusted His headphones, apparently listening to the music and me concurrently. "Yes, the Other Side of God is Pure Creative Energy outside the concepts of time, space, and identity."

I sat up, wiping my wet cheeks, and breathing more calmly. "I couldn't sustain the energy."

"Sustaining it would have shifted your being from separation to wholeness, and you are not finished exploring earth."

I rose on shaky legs. "So the goal is not to ascend earth, but to explore it?"

"We are ascended—already. We are all, always, everywhere. We only have the perception that we are here . . . or there. We are enlightened—already. We are all, always, one. We simply choose to forget, enabling us to adventure into possibilities where we can discover, create, and expand."

"How beautiful," I smiled warmly, "to ascend from the dumpster of feeling unworthy *under* a greater power, to the realization that we are *of* that power."

He nodded lightly and then turned. "Come." He walked, glided actually, into rainbow mist on a floor of compressed air into a warm darkness of seeming night.

I followed. His back appeared the silhouette of steamy prism colors like a wet chalk drawing. My body felt vaporous and soft, not three-dimensional. My mind sank with a sensation as if entering a dream. I doubted that anyone would deem my experience credible because it could not be seen with the outer eye, but it was more credible to me than anything I'd ever done.

He led me to a wall of striking black. Actually, it wasn't a wall. It was the cosmos, outer or inner I could not tell. Like the mirror, it had no beginning or end.

A ray of light crept upon the cosmic view, stretching farther and wider into thousands of light beams. A brilliant sun emerged, white-gold, blood-red, and hot-orange. Colors melded, moving, changing. Enthralled, I said, "Wow!"

He said, "This demonstration can't convey Creative Energy's vastness, but it is a meager attempt at best to aid in further opening the doors within you."

"I understand," I said reverently. He was sharing His findings to deepen mine. I liked that.

"Before you is a symbolic panorama. Creative Energy is not the sun itself, but an image to illustrate my awareness of time and no time. Pure Creative Energy is also the space around the sun, the still behind the chaos, and the emptiness around the fullness—but for now, this image will do."

The volcanically intense power was similar to what I had experienced beyond the veil. My eyes drowned in pleasure.

He said, "Individual beams flood out in all directions, experiencing numerous possibilities simultaneously. There is a sense of individuality between the beams, just as there is a sense of individuality between people, animals, trees—everything."

I nodded with a smile.

He continued, "This sense of separateness gives way to rich explorations of being. I am at point A. You are at point B. I slap your face, you slap mine. I embrace you, you ignore me. I laugh at you, you cry. I smile at you, you smile back. But actually, we are both beyond point A and B, and everything we think we do to each other is only what we *do to ourselves.*"

I said, "So we *are* each other, and only seemingly separate. And all that exists is a part of Creative Energy."

"Not a part of Creative Energy. We each are total Creative Energy. Creative Energy has no parts. Separation is an *impression.*" His orange-socked toes wiggled through the cut openings of His jogging shoes. An invisible force started whirling around Him. Dorothy in the Wizard of Oz tapped her shoes to change her world. I guess My Fool wiggled His toes! The magnetizing force intensified tornado-like, creating a white spinning storm, buzzing loudly. My little bee was far less frightful. I could barely see My Fool through the whirling mass that suctioned me toward it. I resisted, not keen on being devoured. I dug my feet into the ground and hollered, "What's happening?"

A hand popped through the whirl and grabbed my forearm, pulling me into the powerful spin. My hair shot everywhere and the loudness hurt my ears.

I wound up in the calm center. There My Fool and I stood, stable and untouched by the energy whipping around us; however, the buzzing sound remained deafening. I had to shout to hear myself. "What is all this?"

"Be still," My Fool said, "be still within."

I brushed my tangled hair off my face and managed to calm down. The energy that circled us slowed until wheel spokes became visible. The spokes led to a rim that was the object of the whirling.

We were in the hub. The quiet was hauntingly beautiful.

He said, "Like the wheel sustaining many spokes, we are one being with individual selves. One spoke affects the whole wheel. One being affects all beings."

"It's like we are all one great family, and literally too, if you consider we started with a sparse populous that grew into billions."

"Yes. And to brighten the play, each being possesses its own nature, perception, and life experience with a sense of moving forward. The interaction between individuals is charged with thought and emotion, channeled through bodies. Bodies are the main focus. The visual of separation creates the need for language and silence, space and touch. The possession of a body that cries out to survive creates the need for procreation and killing, community and war, the natural world and invention. Yet, each body is encoded with the energy of One. From the vastness, we are born, most forgetting the vastness, born with limits in capability and understanding, born with an intent that begins as a seed and unfolds into a story."

I said, "An intent?"

"The intent is the end of the story before it begins. We experience what we intend to experience even if we are unaware of that intent. The need to fulfill intent is ever present and must be lived."

"Like a purpose for living?"

"Yes. The intent is our 'why' for living. The why is driven by a mandate. The intent to experience poverty might have a mandate of growing up poor to later become a powerful advocate for the deprived. The intent to experience notoriety might have a mandate to become an actress and not lose oneself to image. These are simplifications of course. Branching from the primary intent and primary mandate are multiple sub-intents, and sub-mandates, all in one embodiment. However, as your 'being' is not limited to one body, you concurrently experience other embodiments with other intents and mandates."

"Are you saying that 'my being' is not just experiencing the life of Susan?"

He raised His brows. "I am. Given the concept of time, you as Creative Energy have experienced many embodiments, like one

15

spoke of the wheel to the next and so on. Now, imagine no time. You are the whole wheel all at once."

He opened His hand to my face. I stared into the creases on His palm. I gasped as a hundred tiny faces appeared.

He said, "As you stand before me, you are experiencing many realities, in many times. You are a sixth century Roman Warrior riding a fast horse into battle. You are a peasant in fifteenth-century France scrounging for food. You are a nineteenth-century Russian writer imprisoned for expressing thoughts. You are a twentieth-century Afro American male trying to end prejudice. You are a kidnapped child in Georgia, a depressed housewife in Colorado, a homeless person in India, a nun in France, a baby in an Ethiopian tribe, a hungry dog, a tree, an entity in another dimension. All that you have ever been in this particular train of experience is a part of you currently. Your personality is the sum of that experience. You, Susan, have been long exploring martyr energy, so your sense of self, and freshest memories will carry a martyr tone."

He lowered His palm. The faces lingered in the air. Then they faded into a scene of a nun fetching water from a well. That scene faded into a red-haired youth hunched against prison bars. On and on, brief scenes played before me as He talked.

"Each self in the train of your experience is consciously unaware of what the other selves are doing, where they are, or what time or reality they are in. However, each subconsciously flows through the other's experience as well as their own. Around and around the wheel turns, each spoke influencing the other without realizing it. The flow of these collective experiences influences the conscious decision making of each self."

I saw a mini scene of a man stabbing a woman in the stomach. Next to it, another scene appeared. A woman was clutching her stomach, swigging down Maalox. In another scene, an angelic spirit suddenly feels needed by someone or something, along the lines of a woman stabbed in the stomach, or a woman whose guts are twisting.

I gulped. This was deep. "I am an angelic spirit somewhere?"

"Somewhere . . . we all are." He cleared His throat. "Another story, for another time. Back to the selves in your train of experi-

16

ence. Each self believes his or her reality is the central one. The selves you are now viewing seem like side shows, and you would appear as a side show to them, or perhaps a character in a dream."

I viewed my selves in moments of their daily lives. Tears welled in my eyes. I had a sweeping urge to hug them all. Each one was doing the best they could with the body, time period, and situation they were in. They could do no better. They could do no worse. How noble an experience, this experience of identity! And for the first time, I felt compassionate about my own struggle in the life of Susan. I was doing the best I could, given the cards dealt, and so was everyone else. A wild mercy bloomed inside me. That aching I had felt earlier, the ache born from a cornered dying me, fell away. I had needed to embrace my deep-down self, which was actually pretty crowded—this self few people ever see.

The scenes disappeared.

He wiped a tear from my eye. "There, there."

I said, "If only I had known how hard my selves have struggled, I would have loved me more. If I loved myself more, then maybe my other selves would love themselves more too."

He rested His hand on my shoulder. "Not knowing allows exploration and experience."

My mouth dropped lightly. "Oh, I see. It's kind of like experiencing each unique snowflake, one by one, yet at the same time experiencing all the snow falling at once."

"Yes. While you are always in many places, all places, and no place, and everything that has ever happened, or will happen, is happening right now—your *current focus* will dictate what you will experience."

"So, time seems like time because we focus on a dot and then our whole world becomes the dot. If we move a little to the right then we experience another dot, and this gives the impression of time. If we focused on everything, there would be no time."

"That is a good metaphor, Susan. Your focus this moment is in the deeper world. From here, you can see how individual perception creates judgments. These judgments spawn actions that lead us to explore. What is being explored, or how it's being explored means less than the pure act of simply exploring. In a sense, the set up, or life situation, is created to spark creativity, and the curiosity to explore possibilities. Individuality is the pen that channels Creative Energy into a story. The story of *What would happen if . . . ?* Remove the concept, all concepts, and you have Pure Creative Energy, a blank page with no pen to write a story."

My eyebrows shot up. "So, we are here to explore, not just good things, but also bad things?"

My Fool's hands started conducting to the music pouring from His headphones. "Good and bad, failure and success, weakness and strength, are only agreed-upon perceptions. What is deemed bad, a failure, or weakness in one culture might be deemed good, a success, or a strength in another. An act of yesteryear, while once deemed right, might now be deemed wrong."

As a scholar in human behavior, I knew His words held truth. "Then all that we experience is meant to be; what we perceive as good and bad, though ever changing, is important to the story."

"Precisely." His one hand shot down to the earth and the other toward the sky with a conductor's finality. His body seemed to pulsate energy. "We are seeds that birth into identities who experience harmony and dissonance. What is happy without sad? What is victory without defeat? What is peace without chaos? But, oh . . . look upon the wonders of this earth born of seeds!"

I thought of seeds then, all different kinds growing into different things. And even if a bunch of seeds grew into marigolds, no two marigolds were precisely the same. Oh, how wondrous the birthing of uniqueness! And this thought begged the question. "But, what makes us—us? I mean how are the properties of an identity determined?"

The energy pulsating from His body intensified. Even His violet sweatshirt seemed brighter. His hands waltzed softly with the symphony in His ears. "The identity's *intent* will determine its architectural design. This design is made of references such as fear of crowds, or a fear of being alone. A draw to the great outdoors, or a longing for the metropolis. Being naturally high-strung or stoical, outspoken or shy. References can involve life-long feelings, such as an ever-present sadness, or resounding inner joy. Other forms of reference might involve being empathic or insensitive, narcissistic or self-deprecating, scientifically or artistically minded, retarded or genius. The list of references can be many and varied. These references hold the self right down to eye color, into a location of time and space, and guide its journey to fulfill the identity's intent."

His abstraction was almost too hard to follow. "So, it's like we design our identity to guide us into a particular life experience?"

His musically inclined hands dropped gently to His sides. He sighed. There was great power in His sigh, as if He'd experienced something extraordinary in the music. "Yes, and in the concept of time, each identity's design will feed into the design of the next life experience, like having many bodies in one long life. Certain references, such as narcissism or self-deprecation, can trail over into the next body where the 'being' will continue its experience. Sometimes we come into earth with references or memories from other worlds. In 'no time,' however, everything happens at once. There are stories playing out, right now, all around us where we stand."

I glanced around, a bit spooked, and stepped sideways inadvertently, wondering if I might be standing in someone's invisible presence.

He chuckled, "It's not like that. For an identity to exist, it must have a location in time and space. We can see, and are seen by, only those in *our* location. Location, meaning the vibration of a mind state, one's state of being, or the reality an identity is focused upon. The unseen all around us live in a different reality. One can have a slight momentary shift to another location, and experience for example: the so-called dead, other seemingly non-physical beings, or bleed through experiences from other times and places, or entities that we have been, are, or will be. However, for the most part, we are invisible to all others that are not in our location, and they are invisible to us."

"So, there are many layers of reality, and many identities in each."

"Yes, and all are made up of the same stuff, so the appearance of solidity depends on an identity's location. If contact with another requires a location shift, then one or the other might appear spirit-like, or dream-like because the shift is incomplete. A complete shift would require one or the other to exit their world fully, which would remove them from it. So, a spirit in one world might appear solid in another. It is a matter of perception from the location one is in."

I know I had a stupefied look on my face because air tickled my throat from my open-wide slack jaw.

"And the mystery deepens," He said playfully. "There are also many selves in one identity, not only all the selves you have been or will be, but also many aspects such as mother, father, child, warrior, sage, artist, scientist and so on. These selves support the journey of an identity, just like molecules in a drop of water support the drop, or the crystalline aspects of a snowflake sustain a unique creation."

He made it sound so pretty. I just loved hearing Him speak.

He huffed a little breath of silver sparkles that landed on my face. I couldn't feel them on my skin, but I was suddenly more alert and receptive than I'd ever been. I had a sensation that we'd gone deeper into the center of the wheel, so deep the wheel could no longer be seen.

His words of sharp wisdom cut passage into my ignorance. "Creative Energy—creates. The creations create more creations, and so on. Everything creates and everything is created. The child goes from crawling to walking, to running, ever exploring her talents, curious and desiring experiences. We are always becoming more than we are, and yet we are already all that is."

"So, Creative Energy drives us to have experiences."

"No, it doesn't drive us. We drive us. We are Creative Energy. We are our own creation, even if we don't remember."

I said, "It's like when we feel alone, afraid, or in pain, we often call to something along the lines of 'divine' for connection, faith, and comfort. But what I hear you say is that instead of calling to something *greater and separate* from us, we are really calling for ourselves, like a grain of sand calling for its beach to belong, or a leaf calling for its tree to feel whole."

"Yes," He said, "spiritual beliefs are all valid and necessary for those who believe them no matter what they are. However, constantly transcending the boundaries of those beliefs leads one ever deeper into the bounty of 'totality.' Prayer is a form of calling out to ourselves to remember who we were preceding our experience of separation. We are answered with, but do not always hear, 'It is I. It is I. It is I. Don't you know who I am?' "

I felt like the wind had been knocked out of me. My head felt big and small at the same time. I blinked, unable to speak.

His voice seemed distant, yet close, "In expanded awareness, there is oneness. We are not separate from a perceived Creator." There appeared on either side of Him, a tall tree that disappeared into the clouds, and a clump of violets. His left hand flopped out to the tree theatrically. "The tree is tall." His right hand flopped out to the violets with matched theatrics. "The violets are small." Then, His head cocked to one side. "The tree isn't a clump of violets," and to the other, "and the violets aren't the tree." Looking forward He said, "I'm not you and you're not me." Then He crossed His wrists over His heart pointing fingers at the tree and the violets. "And what would become of this rhyme, if superseding space and time?"

"The two become one," I answered.

He disappeared. Then He came back with a funny little smile on His face.

"How did you do that?"

"For a moment, I . . . un-became."

"But how?"

"Creative Energy perpetually is. It doesn't respond to time or space. The idea of no time, no space, is perhaps impossible for the human mind to fully grasp. It is the way it is supposed to be."

I furrowed my brows. "How can there be no time and space? I get the concept, but still things age, time go by, and centuries pass . . . don't they?"

"Yes, seemingly. However, the impression of time and space comes from no time and no space."

I sighed, a little frustrated by my limited comprehension.

"The time-space focus cements earth reality and human existence. Defocus and you are gone. You get what you see and you see what you get." His eyes turned kaleidoscopic, triangles of patterns moving and changing. I shook my head to make it go away. It was making me dizzy. Then his eyes seemed brown again, gold flecked, and sort of glistening. "Everything is and everything isn't." His left eyelid crouched playfully in the corner of His eye.

I repeated, "Everything . . . is, and everything—"

"Wait a moment," He said, closing His eyes. "Wait a moment. The music . . . ." His hands danced as a symphony conductor once again. I could barely hear the music through His headphones, but I could clearly feel the music through His hands that moved with the music. Though He stood before me, He seemed far away. And though He only left me for a moment, it seemed an eternity.

He opened His eyes and sighed. "Mahler's fifth movement, 3rd Symphony—to me," He shook His head, "speaks volumes."

I wanted to say, 'What? What? Tell me what it said,' when He blurted, "Turn around."

I turned around. A white microscope sat on a brown desk. He moved to my side. "Look into the microscope."

I pushed my eye to the spectacle and viewed a cell and its components.

He said, "This cell is an individual. The particles within the cell are also individuals. If we could create a more powerful instrument, we would see particles within particles, smaller and smaller and smaller. Each particle, each cell, is having its own incarnation. Unlike human consciousness, cells are aware of every other cell, not only in our bodies but also of every cell in the earth and Universe. Cells are encoded with the makings of creation, thus our bodies carry the Universe. Moving the other direction—"

I saw cells splitting, forming bunches of cells.

"—these cells create larger entities, entities that could not be without the smaller units that make them. The smallest speck of energy regales the importance of the cosmos!" The microscope and table disappeared and a boxer dog sat in front of us wagging its tail. "Nice doggie," He said, patting its head. The dog turned into a globe of the earth. He spun the globe hard. "And somewhere, earth is viewed as a cell, and humans, the particles within that cell. Once we become aware of the interconnectedness of all people, places, and things, our current life experience grows wings."

"Life is vast," I said, "incomprehensible really."

"From a standpoint of identity, yes. Just as there are many selves within you, and of you, and around you, they are all layers of one great being. Exploration of identity continues, ever marching to the sea of conclusion where the newness of another perceived reality is born. Creative Energy composes symphonic masterpieces. Synchronistic adventures perpetuate every aspect of being. The assignment is to be—just be."

The globe disappeared.

He said, "Open your knapsack."

I unlatched the fasteners on my russet knapsack. He threw something toward me. It sailed right into the opening. I glanced at the object nestled in the bristles on my brush. It was a yellow gem.

He said, "That is the Gem of Perception."

The gem began glowing, spraying rays of golden light that brightened as He talked.

He said, "Perceive this: You and everything that makes you is a work of beauty. Inside you, a light flickers, not yet shining its full potential. Thick clouds of facade dim the brilliance. Eventually, your light will melt facade and envelop your world. With your intent fulfilled, the Universe will shine brighter." His arms stretched wide, opening to all the world. No, just opening. "This day of days, after a night of nights, walk the winds." Then He smiled, cheeks puffed with joy. He reminded me of Happy in Snow White and the Seven Dwarves. His arms jolted like a conductor with each word. "Ain't—Life—Great!" He turned away from me, and walked toward a flowery meadow.

I shouted, "Don't leave!"

His head twisted back slightly. "Just perceptions."

"Where are you going?" I called.

"To watch groundhogs."

"But—"

Without looking back, He waved goodbye.

I wanted to follow My Fool, but somehow I knew I had to follow myself and find my own way.

And so do you.

To this end, expand your perception of yourself and the world. Reminisce for a moment the familiar words that roll around inside your head on days of anguish. Words like, 'Why me? It isn't fair. I've been cheated. I'm bad. It's a cruel world. God is punishing me. There is no God, faith, or hope. I have failed. I am not loved. I don't measure up.' And the most futile of all pleas, 'If only.'

All these phrases are but perceptions of reality. *Perceptions* of reality. Think. The condition of your existence is based on what *you* perceive. How do you view yourself, the world, life? Don't rush this answer. Close your eyes and ponder. Hey, close those eyes!

Now that you possess at least a vague awareness of these answers, you know where you are. Now that you know where you are, you can choose to move from that point. To do this, you must release perceptions of yourself, the world at large, and life. You must release these perceptions no matter how profound, superficial, or safe they may be.

Though all perceptions are partly true, none are wholly true, for they are based subjectively on *one* point of view. The objective here is to see all life at once, not a perception, but all perceptions in one glorious gaze.

Open your mind to the idea that good and bad are subjective. All action breeds consequences. Natural Law brings all to balance. What happens to you is less significant than *what you do* with what happens to you. Your reactions will define your life experience. What part did you play in the creation of an event? How have you helped make your life what it is? If you want to change it, what can you do?

Ponder deeply. Spend time in ponder mode, despite your outer world activities. Deep inside you resides a sage. Ask your inner sage these loaded questions. Your sage will answer. *Always* your sage will answer. Did you know that? Now that you do, you hold the key to liberation. What you do with that key is truly and solely–your choice.

Into the Night
"The Dream is Life. Life's the Dream."

GEM#2 ALTERNATE REALITIES

I hiked the idyllic countryside into a forested area that thickened as I contemplated how I create my reality. Contemplation is most often a quiet place, this concentration on extracting from depths what is not seen in the light.

So many levels. So many actions. Conscious thinking seemed to complicate my effort and impede my findings. The forest grew thicker, darker, and a bit ominous. As evening crept in around me and shadow played with moonlight, I sighted a cavern opening guarded by a daunting sticker bush. I pushed past the precarious thicket assaulted by relentless thorns that seemed to say, 'Do not trespass.' I did trespass however, in desperate need of rest and a safe haven in which to meet that need. I entered the shallow cave and sighed. I would be safe here in my hiding place.

Safety was a large issue with me. Oh, not so much physical safety or even emotional, it was more that I had trouble standing up for my needs and my dignity, and I was not all that handy at blocking the psychological punch. Hence, hiding held great appeal.

My entire body ached with exhaustion. I stuffed my knapsack under my head and lay on the solid surface that soothed my aching back. I pinched a nerve some years ago while a foreboding boss, positioned behind me, watched me type labels for him. How and why did I make that happen? How and why did I create the reality of an aching back? I had to be good for him you know, had to be good, and my back reminded me everyday.

Slumber took me swiftly. Drifting into that sweet dreamland, the curtain to myself opened. I glimpsed the collective as a great play, commingling and repelling, creating stories of joy and woe. Characters solid and yet changing in the silent glow of their unconscious intent—sometimes the savior, sometimes the victim, and sometimes the perpetrator.

A scene formed. I stood sobbing in ragged clothes in a ravaged land. Ailing angry people crowded around me, accusing me of this horrific circumstance. I bolted awake from the dream, shouting, "No!" as I sat up in the dark. No. No more blaming, not myself, not others. I would rise above the subjective viewpoints that assign blame. Whose fault is this or that? As a psychotherapist, I had long learned that beneath the mask of fault lies innocence of the flailing and the lost, but mostly—the afraid. And I was no different. The compassion extended to others, I must now extend to myself. I willed myself to dream differently, that I may journey well into the mysterious inner sanctum of my being.

I rested my back on the cavern floor once more, head on knapsack, not to re-experience what my dream had turned into—the familiar martyr-victim struggle that was my daily life. This time, I traversed the collective of players and the play I had first seen. I sank deeper into the thick balmy waters of a richer dream. In the dream, My Fool found me resting in the very cave my body was sleeping. His headphones cupped my ears in warm comfort, and His Walkman was clipped to the waist of my blue jeans. The entreating horns in Richard Strauss's *Alpine Suite* seem to speak to me in ways even the best of words cannot connote, but it went something like this: "The surface world manifests from its conception in dream worlds."

In the dream, I opened my eyes, eager to tell My Fool about the insight that I'd gained from the music. I gasped. Humongous lips covered my field of vision. His lips. I scrunched my eyes shut. But even with eyes closed, the lips remained. I almost wanted to wake up just to get a grip.

He said, "The conscious world is not as tangible as one might think and not the best arena to get a grip."

"Your lips are huge," I said, like a frightened little girl.

"That is because you invest so much in what I say, so my mouth seems large. If you realized that I am but a conduit of your inner sage, that all I say is you speaking to yourself, you will find my lips

26

shrinking to a comfortable size."

I peeked at Him once again and His whole face was there. Better. Much better. I sat up. "So the dream world is where we can get a grip on our lives?"

He pushed His hand through the rock wall like a ghost and pulled it back. "Our daily lives dim awareness. The altered state of sleep heightens awareness." With His back to the wall He looked like He was going to sit, but His behind went through the wall and came back again when He stood. I wanted to ask Him why He was doing that, but I feared interrupting His train of thought. "The dream world is present twenty-four hours a day. We do not go to it when we sleep. We step out of it when we are awake, but it does not go away. We simply become unaware of it."

"Wow," I said. "I never thought of it like that before."

He continued, "Our daily lives are projections from the dream world. The dream is Creative Energy creating."

"So, we come from the dream? And, in a way, we slide into conscious reality each day to perform what has been created in the unconscious?"

"Yes. All conscious living comes from the unconscious, including ideas, inventions, solutions, and prophecies. Meaningful experiences flower in the outer world because their roots draw sustenance from deeper states of being. Music is heard in the composer's head before it is played in the concert hall. The intent of an identity exists before it is experienced. If we do not 'go within' the conscious world grows foggy, yielding but opaque awareness influenced by outer world perceptions. Our identity cannot survive, nor fulfill its intent, without dipping into dream worlds."

I was about to respond profoundly when He playfully turned sideways and dipped His head into the rock wall and back with a Charlie Chaplin smile. And just when I was about to laugh He said seriously, "The unconscious self in sleep is aware of the conscious self operating in the concrete world, and is in constant communication with it. And the conscious self must rest in the dream worlds to work out the dramas of its daily life."

"That makes sense," I said. "From practicing psychotherapy, I have discovered that in dreams, true feelings find expression. Fear can play out as monsters chasing you. Anger can play out as you chasing the monsters. Dreams reflect conscious life. Also, players in the dream are often aspects of one's self. Like if you dream of a shy woman, she can represent the shy part of you. Even a person you know, like an uncle who is ultra logical, can represent the ultra logical part in you. Or a critical parent in a dream can be a reflection of being self-critical."

He tilted His head and stared at me. "You are doing it again."

"What?" I said, looking around sheepishly.

"Trying to uphold the image of the dutiful student, the good and smart little girl."

"I am, aren't I? Why do I keep doing that?"

"Come, I'll show you." He turned to the cavern wall.

I rose, and watched Him walk through rock. I followed, but banged my head.

"I thought this was a dream," I grumbled, rubbing my forehead. "I'm supposed to be able to walk through walls."

He reached out, and pulled me through.

"How come I couldn't do that?"

"Because you fear going deeper." His eyes glittered. "I've been here many times, but it never looks the same. Sometimes I get lost trying to get out."

I furrowed my brows and said sarcastically. "Wonderful."

We walked in red-black dark through a rock tunnel. "Where are we going?"

"To meet your nature."

"My nature? That's not like meeting your maker is it?"

"In a way, yes."

I widened my eyes. "Yes?"

"Uh, huh," He said casually.

"Uh, huh," I repeated and bit my lower lip.

"Your nature helps direct your life story. For instance, I have a warrior nature. You have a martyr nature."

"If we want to change our nature," I asked, "can we?"

He raised a brow. "One's nature can be modified, but not nullified, not as long as one's identity remains intact."

"Why?"

"A nature is needed to cement the reality of an identity. Dissolving one's nature would dissolve one's identity, which exists to ensure fulfillment of an intent."

I rolled my eyes. "Oh great. So, I am stuck with a martyr nature."

"Not stuck, not necessarily. How will you use this nature? And why do you have it?"

He had a point. I had my nature for a reason, and I could learn to use it differently. I adjusted the headphones on my ears. The music had heightened, competing with our conversation. "Can I remove these headphones?"

"Yes," He said, "but you will lose your way if you do."

I scowled, thinking I hadn't even found my way yet, and what kind of trouble I'd be in if I lost it too!

He said, "In time, you will hear the music naturally, without headphones. But . . . until then—"

"Can *you* hear the music naturally?"

"Yes."

"Why do you need headphones?"

"They remind me to listen."

I was going to ask Him more about hearing music naturally, when we rounded a corner.

"Are you ready to meet your maker," He chuckled, "I mean nature?"

I was terrified, yet excited. A part of me wanted to turn back to safety, but a greater part of me wanted to go forward and find myself.

He whistled casually, His tone harmonizing with a whimsical part of the symphony.

I have to admit, the tune calmed me.

His whistle turned to words. "This is where I met my nature, in the form of a red-eyed power monger."

Away with the calm. I gulped, wondering what 'I' was going to meet.

The tunnel opened into a stark gray cell. Sorrow drenched cold walls. I saw the back of a nun in a black habit, sitting on her knees, hands in prayer position over her cot.

I knew who she was. She was the me that found worth by abasing myself and meeting everyone's needs, but never my own. I could help others, but they were not allowed to help me. It was my *nature* to starve and suffer for all, for I could feel their pain and I so desperately wanted to ease it. Maybe if I suffered for them, their suffering would cease. This was a state of mind that I not only knew so well, but also in which I was most comfortable. Looking at myself that way, I felt strangely disturbed.

I wanted to shake My Nun nature out of that delusion, hug her, feed her, and make her take this journey into wholeness with me. I walked up behind her expecting to create a tender moment between us, but to my surprise, she rose and whipped around with Dracula eyes stretched open before the bite! "You are mine!"

She grabbed me. I shrieked. She pulled me *inside* her ghostly presence. I screamed, popping out my head and one arm. She was becoming solid, and I the ghost! I called to Him. "Save me!"

He answered coolly, "You must save yourself." His eyes drew inward. "When this happened to me—"

There I was, gobbled by a Nun, gasping for breath, and He was babbling about His past.

"—it was the Mongolian Warlord, my red-eyed power monger, who tried to possess me. I commanded he cease running the show, controlling everyone, and coercing them to live by his opinion. I told him his behavior kept us in a stagnating pattern that would end us both. He did not interrupt. In fact, he didn't even reply. He ignored me as if he'd not heard me and continued running the show. A lot of good pleading my case did. I felt more possessed by him than ever."

My head was pulled back into The Nun. She rammed my face into her wounded heart thick with agony. I tasted blood and pus. Nausea gripped my stomach. This I could not digest, would not, not any more! I was drained dry suffering for the world. With sheer willpower, I pushed my face back out of her, giving her the appearance of a two-headed nun.

"Oh, there you are," He said, and continued His story. "I continued dialoging with the Mongolian Warlord who kept bombarding my wife with reasons why she should follow his instructions for living. I cornered him within me, and delivered so convincing an argument, Patton himself would have laid down arms. I sighed deeply, feeling a great sense of accomplishment. 'Well?' I said to him. He glared stoically at my face and replied, 'My way is the right way.' He brushed me aside and marched back to my wife to finish what he had started. I trailed behind him, unable to stop his lips from flapping. My poor wife. She sat there in a heap."

My face turned lobster red. I was being crushed!

On He chattered. "I finally threw reason to the wind, and com-manded. 'You *will* bow down.' Not only did The Warlord retain dominion, He also gained strength, contemplating who would win the World Series, how to make another million dollars, and how weak everyone was to not take control of their problems and force them to be solved! Oh yes, I know what it's like to be swallowed by your nature."

"Is this supposed to help me?" I cried. "What should I do!"

He shrugged His shoulders. "Experiment."

The Nun was sucking my head back in. I strained to keep it out, feeling pressure build along my spinal chord. I wondered briefly if that was why I had so many back problems.

I shouted, "Help me! I think she's going to break my neck."

"I told you, you must help yourself."

"How do I escape!"

"From your nature?" He shook His head, "Can't."

"What am I supposed to do!"

"Figure it out."

"How! What did you do?" I screamed.

"Ah, what did 'I' do?"

He replied, calm as ever, so calm that seconds were ticking for me like hours. "Well, first, I stopped dialoguing with my nature. 'I' attuned myself to Creative Energy, the totality, *The All*. I used the tool of a symphony, and moved into the energy of the music. I was lifted from the drama and experienced the overview."

I quit fighting The Nun, my martyr nature, and shifted my at-tention to the music playing in my ears, Richard Strauss's *Alpine Suite*. I closed my eyes and let myself fall into The Nun, focusing only on the music. The music had built into a climactic compilation of the tunes of many instruments, and I gave myself to it. My whole being seemed to drop endlessly into the bottomless pit of My Nun's heart—chinked, gouged, and smothered with grotesque wounds.

I had clarity then. My nature was to choose suffering because if I didn't, I'd have to confront anger, learn to defend myself, and step out into the world. I'd have to be a warrior and that was the last thing on earth I wanted to do. Learning to use the yang energy for self-defense was sinful to My Nun. And hence, though it made no sense to the psychotherapist in me, or what I would deem the healthy part of me, it did exist—this choice of eternal suffering that would somehow keep me 'pure.' The cloistered nun symbolized my nature perfectly. She was my nature. She was.

Protection was my deepest desire. But if I had to take up arms to protect myself, I'd rather suffer. And I always did. When would I defend myself? When? It occurred to me then that the very arms My Fool was trying to lay down, were the arms I desperately needed to embrace. I needed audacity, and He compliance. But why did we possess these natures? Before I could go deeper, the scene changed as a slow beautiful note ended Strauss's *Alpine Suite*.

We were back by the cavern entrance. I was positioned on the cavern floor in the pose I'd fallen asleep, but my eyes were open, and the headphones had disappeared, now over His ears, and the Walkman on His waist.

His voice held whimsy, "You sure hightailed it out of there!"

He was again standing over me, His body in a yellow glow.

I asked, "Is the dream over?"

He shook His head. "The dream is never over."

"I mean, are we back in consciousness?"

"Why rush to get back?"

"Cause this is scary."

He shrugged His shoulders. "Let's go back."

I sat up. "No, wait, I don't want to go back."

"Let's stay," He said. "There is much to explore." He sat in front of me, ankles crossed.

I sighed nervously, crossing my legs in a half lotus. "All right, what's next?"

His golden glowing body dimmed. We were face to face in the

velvet dark. His faint facial features seemed to change as He talked. "Dreams are a window for examining one's journey in the mundane world, as well as a stage to experiment, consequence free. What would happen if we did this, or that? What would happen if this or that occurred? Upon awakening, our life choices are influenced by our dream experience, whether we realize it or not."

"So, if I fear my boss, I might dream various scenarios of dealing with that situation. The dreams lend a sense of how to handle my problem. Like that?"

"Like that," He echoed. "Further, once pent up emotions find release in the dream world, then that expelled energy blends with Creative Energy to whip up a new brew to be projected back into the mundane world."

His face kept changing, as if I were looking at Him through moving water.

"Hmm." I said, "So energy never dies; it is just transformed."

"Transformed," He repeated in a trance-like state. Liquid ripples seemed to cross His face. I could barely view His lips move. "Dreams are never so simple as they seem, for they are a multi-level experience."

"In what way?"

Words came from His watery face. "You might dream you are in a dentist's chair having your overly sharp dog-shaped canines filed down. Level One: You watched a T.V. show on dentistry that evoked symbols for your dream. Level Two: You get ferocious when you feel vulnerable, as when a dentist works on your teeth. Or, you have a vicious dog-like anger that needs to be trimmed. Or, you are cutting back on saying mean things. Level Three: You are doing deep work on yourself, transforming dog-like energy into a calmer way of being. Level Four: The experience of another is impacting your dream while you impact theirs. Level Five: You are exploring the reality of your other selves, and they are exploring yours. "

"That's a lot," I said.

"And that is not all, but the other levels will be another story for another time. Now if you are a dentist or are married to a dentist or have had bad experiences with a dentist, the dreams significance will have a different twist than another having the same dream without these associations."

"So," I said, "one dream can have multiple meanings, and the same dream could have different meanings to different people."

"Yes, and you are your own best interpreter, because no one else experiences or perceives life exactly like you. And if you listen to your dreams, they can help you find direction."

"Like a compass?"

"Very much so. However, we don't have to adhere. Our choices are part of the adventure. Yet, our lives might ease if we follow that inner guidance. This is not to be confused with the idle chatter of the dream characters within us, such as pacifist, power monger, or vigilante. Their perspectives are skewed. Beyond them dwells the core self in a pool of Pure Creative Energy that never forgets it is *beyond* all identities, or shall we say, *of* all identities. Drawing from this pool, we move in directions that *feel* healing, and sometimes defy logic."

"So, the deepest levels of the dream world can connect us to a purer essence untainted with skewed perceptions."

"Yes. This deeper connection can occur while retaining identity in the mundane world. Identity is necessary to have a personalized story to fulfill an intent. This is one reason we mostly forget those deeper experiences once we surface to the conscious world."

"So, do we benefit even if we don't remember, or understand our dreams?"

"Yes. Dream worlds, remembered or not, understood or not, provide fuel for conscious living. And what we attain from conscious living is expelled in our dreams. In return, our dreams impart guidance, insight, and wisdom that emerges in our daily lives. We might blurt out something wise. Where did it come from? Well, it came from the part of us that is always located in altered states. Remembering and paying attention to dreams, however, can enhance these gifts and heighten self-understanding."

When He said that, silvery beings fell out of Him and trailed high, like upward shooting stars through the cavern ceiling. "What just came out of you!"

"Those are the other me's exploring different possibilities in dreams."

I shook my head. "This is confusing."

"Imagine a thousand Susans living out every possible reality. In each reality, the other possibilities are but a dream to the dreamer. So what you live out in your daily life is but a dream to another Susan in another world."

I was most puzzled. I felt like Elmer Fudd trying to get a hold on Bugs Bunny's psyche.

He continued, "In dreams, not only can you visit the playing of possibilities through other Susans, but you can also journey to any point in time or space of this Susan, where the long-term effects of your choices can be viewed."

Though His insights were overwhelming, they also were somehow changing me, opening me, deepening me.

He said, "There is no need to understand it all, Susan. Sensing the magnitude of the dream world is enough. The dream brings stories big and small into form. Life can't exist, earth can't exist—without dreams. All people, places, and things dream, experiencing connection with all others in the dream. Then dreams hold the earth and its contents together. All concepts flow through the dream state."

His face changed into many faces. His voice seemed to take on many languages, yet the meaning still reached me. It was about travel to other realities and unearthly worlds. Then His words became clear. "When you sleep, the dreams you have . . . are real and more connected to conscious life than most can imagine."

I murmured, "The dream is life, and life's the dream." My head seemed to open. A brilliant pyramid light went inside me. I felt like I'd received something, but I didn't know what. Then I came to consciousness, my back flat on the cavern floor.

I stretched as one does when waking from a long slumber. I rolled to my side, adjusting my pack under my head for comfort. I jumped a little when I saw My Fool's face staring at me, the watery effect gone. He was lying on His side, parallel to my body. Moonbeam slivers filtered through the brambles of the cave entrance and barely gave Him shadow.

I mumbled, "I feel like I just had a meditative experience."

He continued talking to me as if I hadn't even come to consciousness. I found that strange.

He said telepathically, "The dream world is present twenty-four hours a day, remember? Even in consciousness, one can shift focus and find it."

For a moment, I felt the boundaries between the conscious and unconscious disappear.

His voice came through. "Like dreams, meditation is a gateway to the unconscious where physical reality is born. Meditations can be as simple as staring at a sunset and being truly present, to experiencing deeper worlds of wisdom and beauty. Optimally, the idea is to still the conscious mind and leave *all* perceptions at the door, from self-image to the very belief systems one might live by. Enter the deeper realm empty and open to truth beyond all beliefs. Walk into your vast self beyond all conscious conception.

"Nature and or music are great catalysts. If you do not release beliefs (at least temporarily), though the experience can be intense, your interpretation of the meditation will reflect your belief system. If ten people had the experience of seeing a great being speak wisdom, the vision of that being would appear different to each. If you believed that a religious icon is sacred, you would see the great being as that icon, be it an animal, element, or of human persona. For instance: if you believe that chipmunks are gods, then your sacred being would look like a chipmunk. If possible, transcend all beliefs. Stay fluid. Stay open. Never seal the deal with, 'I experienced *the* truth!' Rather say, 'I experienced *a* truth.' This openness can allow even greater wisdom and beauty to enter."

"Wow, what a fantasy that would be."

"Fantasizing is the other way we enter altered states."

"Fantasizing?" I said, "I find that not too important, beyond revealing basic psychological needs."

Suddenly, I dropped from the cave, back first, plunging down into a long well. "I feel like I am still dreeeeaming!" I cried to Him on my way down.

He shouted back playfully, "You mean that you feel like your dreeeeaming in the awaaake staaate?"

"Yeeeesss." I hit bottom, plunging into a pile of down feathers that puffed up all around me. Since my mouth was open on the way down, a feather got stuck to my tongue. I pulled it off with distaste.

I couldn't see Him, but His voice was clear. "These feathers are your fantasies. Fantasies are created in the deep wells of your personal truth, or shall we say, your identity's intent. What is a fantasy but the deepest, truest longing of any individual? A fantasy holds more truth than conscious existence that tells us to snap out of it and do something real—like the laundry, homework, fix the shower door, lift weights, play cards, go to a movie. Are these acts more important than a daydream?"

A black and white feather floated down on my forehead, landing—just so. A fantasy I often had took form before my eyes. *A brave warrior teaches me his skills of shrewd self-defense. I teach him the glories of soul connection.*

My Fool continued speaking in a scholarly fashion, while I felt ridiculous. "Your fantasy reveals your need to become male-female balanced. Your fantasies keep you in touch with your true desires."

A bright red feather landed under my nose. I sneezed. Suddenly, rage blazed through me.

He said, "Sometimes your fantasies help you release anger."

I visualized my warrior confronting a man who had hurt me.

A blue feather fell on my heart. Sadness overcame me. I visualized preparing to jump off a windy cliff to my death, when my warrior apprehends me and says he will help me fight my demons.

I realized then that I had Warrior on the Brain. I was a little embarrassed that He knew.

He must have understood my discomfort, because He removed me from the spotlight for a moment. His voice sounded next to my ear, even though I was at the bottom of this strange well. "Men, for instance, sometimes fantasize that multiple women engulf them with sexual energy. If you were a man and that was your fantasy—" Darn Him. I felt like a man. "—what are you needing? Validation of your sexuality? Does sexual validation make you feel more worthy?"

I kept telling myself, "I'm a woman. I'm a woman." But somewhere inside me I knew that some part of me was a man, so I tried to dissolve my barriers of resistance and flow with His words.

"Why do you, as a man, feel unworthy? You can trace that feeling to its roots. What thoughts hold that feeling in place? When were those thoughts born? Perhaps when you were seven years old, you began noticing that television abundantly portrayed women loving men by giving them sex. Television gave you the message that your lovability is measured by the number of women who want to bed you. So, for years you ingrained that notion in your head. Do you secretly feel unloved? Are you trying to live up to the image of the macho stud you see in fiction? What if, instead, you embraced your essence from the deepest core of your being, and unleashed more Creative Energy. You would not only be at peace with your worth, but others would be attracted to you like moths to a flame."

That made sense. I thought of athletes and actors. Either I'd read His mind or He read mine. I guess it didn't matter. I decided to relax in my well of fantasy, and be open to discovery.

He said, "Why do we admire actors? We admire them because they are shining Creative Energy. That is what makes them look beautiful. Why do we admire athletes? Because they are shining Creative Energy. That is what makes them appear dazzling. Would you be so attracted if you saw them in their duller moments—the actress screaming at her spouse, or the athlete tripping over a chair? You don't generally see them like this, so you become a fan, envisioning them with god-goddess status. You watch them when they shine. You can shine too. You too can achieve a radiant status, whether the opposite sex embraces you or not. What people are really fantasizing is themselves basking in Creative Energy. Even if the fantasy is not probed for deeper meaning, it reveals something fundamental about yourself. Is that less valid than doing dishes?"

I imagined dirty dishes stacked in my sink, and on counters up to the ceiling, piling high all around my house, because all I did was fantasize. I started to laugh.

He said, "There will always be dishes to do, and they will always get done, and undone, over and over. Whatever do you gain by basing your sense of achievement on getting them done? What have you achieved? Again, what is your worth based on? Outer world achievements? Outside approval? Meeting social criteria?"

I nodded lightly to myself, realizing how much I sought outside approval, a bit humiliated that I was so needy. He didn't shame me though. He was a teacher. The best.

His voice intensified. Each word cut into me. "In the concrete world, you live a confusing dream ever trying to remember *who you are* in a world that tells you *what to be*. Sleep . . . and you will find who you are! Daydream . . . and you'll realize what you are trying to be."

Then I was sitting in the cave again. I felt like I was at Disneyland going on one ride after another. "So, though awake, I can be aware of the constant dream state."

"The instant you crossed the State Line, your awareness shifted to the deeper levels of existence *before* physical manifestation."

I sighed, still having difficulty absorbing so much abstraction.

After a weighted pause, He said, "Open your knapsack."

I fumbled in the dark, opening my sack. He dropped a purple gem inside. "That is the Gem of Alternate Realities. It is made of all things, and all things are made of it."

The gem was dazzling, radiating intensely, and blasting deep purple light rays throughout my knapsack. The bristles on my toothbrush seemed to come alive. My sunglasses played live scenes on the lenses. The plum colored shine made the yellow gem seem like a living golden ocean. I shook my head. This couldn't be real. I said something then, that maybe He was thinking. "We purposefully limit our awareness, to explore what we would not, if we *knew*."

"Yes," He said. "The reason for conscious living is to have *experiences*. Creative Energy wants to create. Our society tells us the goal is happiness. But it isn't. Not really. The goal is to experience and to behold the change born from that experience. The drive for happiness is the catalyst that brings us into having experiences, ever growing new limbs to the tree."

I briefly saw holographic scenes where His face would be if I could see it: a man shooting a machine gun, a cave man hunting, and a man opening a door to let in a kitten. His words comforted me. Somewhere amidst all the confusion of daily life, I could see clearly the importance of just 'being.' By just 'being,' we create.

His voice was warm. "As humans, we always long for what we do not know, even when we fear venturing beyond the safe ground of our well established boundaries. If we knew where every road would take us, where would the thrill be? How many roads would we not take? How many experiences would we miss because we knew too much?"

I nodded. "I can relate to that. I've had many hard knocks that helped me mature. If I knew that I was going to get hit, I might have hid from life and remained the 'frightened little girl.' "

"Precisely. Every knock catalyzes us to learn how to heal. Imagine investing in a business proposition, knowing you'd go bankrupt. You probably wouldn't do it. Then you'd miss the experience of taking a chance, rising above humility, the emergence of buried issues with your spouse that need airing, learning the value of inner wealth. All that experience might be lost if we knew we were to embark on a harrowing journey, a journey that gives us so much."

My heart felt big. Hardship yielded great gifts.

He continued, "Enduring hardship, we are enlivened, challenged, forced to find who we are and what we are made of, but most importantly we now know what it feels like to experience a failed business venture, a relationship gone wrong, a loved one dying. We are wiser, stronger, and even changed by the experience. In the end, going through the hell of it, brings us to the heaven of it. And between hell and heaven is a magnificent story."

I nodded, almost feeling teary at the splendor of the human experience. "So really, every path holds an experience. Therefore, no matter what path we take, we are always right?"

"Yes, it's not the path you tread, it's *how* you tread the path. Do you want to tread this or that path? Do or don't. It doesn't matter, for eventually all paths are tread by the multiple you's in the concept of space and time."

I narrowed my eyes absorbing the notion. I liked it. "I see," and I did, even in the dark.

He rose. I heard His knees crack. "Close your knapsack, and let us walk out into the night air."

I was reluctant, not wanting to lift my eyes from the magnificent purple gold that brought my pack to life. Oh well, I could look more later. I started to grab the flashlight in my sack.

"No," He said. "We don't need artificial light to see each other. Leave that artificial light off. Your feet will take you where you want to go, if you trust them."

I abandoned my flashlight, and closed my knapsack. Leaving my pack on the ground, I stood up. "Okay feet, take me."

As He spoke, I realized I could hear Him better by not seeing His face. Outer vision truly can blind inner vision.

We rose, and exited the cave. My feet took me past the sticker bush, less dense than before, and not grabbing my clothes. Was the entrance to myself more opened now?

"This night of nights," He said with outstretched arms, "walk the winds."

Something from deep inside me filled my limbs.

My Fool said, "Go with it. Trust the Creative Life Energy to free your mind from interpreting. Let it move you."

His words played like a symphony, reminding me of Alan Hovhaness's *Symphony No. 22, City of Light*. I couldn't hear the music, but I could feel its rhythm inside me. My body yearned to move! I released myself to the moment and whirled around in amazement. The forest had thinned to a cedar tree here and there.

"All people, places, and things are states of being—including the plants, rocks, dirt, and air. Even your car and the shoes you wear are in a state of being. Everything is."

I stopped whirling and laughed, envisioning my tennis shoes thinking of the feet they knew so well, jogging them through gooey mud. They tighten on my feet with a pinch and declare, "That's for getting us wet!"

"Not so far off," He said. "Someone created those shoes. The very fabric is filled with Creative Energy. The Creative Energy gave them form, and a life, a life with your feet, jogging through mud. Ever have a pair of shoes you love and don't want to give up, even though they are ripping at the seams? You form a relationship with these inanimate objects, because they are the stuff of creation. Creative energy exists in everything, all the time, in a trillion forms. The creations are born of the dream."

A "Webster's Collegiate Dictionary" appeared before my face, on the page that defined—dream. Dream: 1. A series of thoughts, images, or emotions occurring during sleep. 2. An experience of waking life having the characteristics of a dream.

Whoa, even the dictionary implies that the dream is life and life's the dream. Of course, I, being in an altered state, didn't know if the definition was real, or the same as in the concrete dictionary. But then, even if it didn't match conscious reality, who's to say that it's not a valid definition? Besides, whether awake or asleep, I was beginning to experience both worlds in the same way, packed with strange visions, multi-level occurrences, and revelations. Perhaps I *was* dissolving the boundaries between the conscious and unconscious. I felt buoyant. I wanted to whirl some more and dance in the moonlit night.

The book slammed shut. His voice became effervescent. "Whirl, child, whirl!"

Hovahness's symphony now played in my head, as a memory, not naturally, as My Fool said it would one day. I released my inhibitions. Oh, what did it matter if I appeared the fool? Life was here for me to experience, to create, to know myself! Joy sprang in my limbs. I danced gleefully. I dipped and glided, up and down. The wind caressed my face, blowing strands of my long hair in a flurry about my dancing body in the warm night air. I loved my precious legs and my precious heart.

I had a vision as I leapt into the air with a tour jeté. *I was a young French woman in wartime medieval England. I stepped out of the woods onto a path. My dress was torn, my face dirty. My curly red hair gave me a Shirley Temple look. I was following an English knight in chain mail. I followed him because I feared being raped in the woods by a gang of soldiers. He turned around and eyed me with irritation. I said with a thick French accent, "I give you what you want, I follow?" He nodded.*

The vision ended when I came down from my jeté and landed on my feet. I sank to my knees, and hunched over with a heart stopping realization.

The knight was my current husband. I had made a soul contract with him: I would give him my body if he'd protect me. I suddenly realized how that ancient contract was *still* the basis of our relationship. Whenever one of us wanted more, problems arose.

I would never see my husband the same after that vision. Neither one of us had broken the contract. We couldn't, not until we figured out what it was. Only then, could our marriage have a chance of changing, or expanding.

I panted gently, my hands rubbing over soft grasses on the damp earth.

I needed to digest my experience, but His words washed over it. "Dreams, meditations, and fantasies are a fruitful place where one can see a clearer picture of reality, create without outer world obstruction, and experience without the conscious walls that hold one in a governed box."

His words settled inside my brain, wrapping up my adventures for the evening. "These deeper states then, are perhaps the most important levels of the human experience. They are not hideouts. They are where we begin to make our conscious dreams come true." He paused and said, "Ain't—Life— Great!"

He stopped talking. I turned to see Him, but He was gone. He left me alone with myself under the stars.

And this is how I leave you—alone. Alone to fly the dream worlds. Alone to meditate, to consider your fantasies, and feel your longings. I leave you alone to sleep with the intent of discovering yourself through dreams, meditation, and fantasy.

Bon voyage! For now.

Crossing Mud Lake
"Don't think who you are. You're not who you think."

GEM #3 IMAGE

My eyes opened. The sun blared overhead. I squinted, twisting my stiff back. The damp grass had soaked through my blue tee shirt that stuck to my skin. I stretched, opening myself to a new day, and sat up with a yawn. The cedar trees were gone. It seemed that when my state of mind changed, the scenery around me did too.

Grassy plains melded into green hills lit by noon rays. I had slept long. I rose and brushed the dirt from my blue jeans. There was a hole starting over my knee. My apparel was wearing thin. A grasshopper jumped on my brown hiking shoe, as if to say, "Hello," or "I'll meet you again one day," or more like, "I know something you don't know," or maybe I was just nuts. Then my fat green friend hopped away toward the hills. As long as he didn't hop on me! It *seemed* like a nice day.

I combed my fingers over my long brown hair freeing bits of meadow shrubbery from the tangled mass. My heart thudded with apprehension. What would this day reveal? The inner world was rich with surprise.

I walked toward the cave to retrieve my hairbrush from my knapsack. Each step left me feeling less and less like the me I'd known myself to be. I was in no man's land, despite how the outer world perceived me. Oh, to them, maybe I was sitting at my computer, grocery shopping, or driving the kids to lessons, but that's not where I was. That's not where I was at all.

The cave opening had changed. The sticker bushes were more or less gone. Only a few sprigs remained. Self-exploration was getting easier. I paused a moment, staring at the dry brown sticker sprigs. My life used to be just like them, full of burs and irritation.

Society told me, I was a woman who must marry a man who can protect and provide for me. In return, I must have babies, raise kids, keep the house clean, look sexy, make frequent love to my husband, and if possible . . . make money. I could get an education as long as I didn't rock the boat. And I could have a career as long as I didn't make waves. I must be devoted, honest, and obedient to the government of the United States of America. I was to make money, pay taxes, and fashion my kids to be compliant, upstanding citizens. I was to stay thin and young and look pretty to men forever.

"And I—" His voice sounded behind me.

I turned around. There My Fool stood, headphones on ears, holding a rowboat paddle. I was a little distracted by the sight, not hearing His words like I'd wanted and later wished I had. "—was told I was a man who should rise above emotions and never take a passive stance. I was told to acquire a pretty wife, and raise pretty kids, and make a pretty penny to have a pretty house, car, and bank account. Once I acquired those things, I didn't want to stop 'getting.' But no matter how much I got, I never had myself. And even when I gave up the role society bid me perform, I found another role to play. I played the spiritual guru. Oh, I thought the new role was the real me, but it was just another facade, a mask I wore to keep me from myself. With each mask I shed, a new one formed. I peeled away mask after mask, after mask, like onion layers that have no end. And there were times when these facades competed for my attention. What mask would I wear today? What role would I play?"

I didn't realize how buried in masks My Fool once was. Even I didn't have *that* many.

His eyes glittered. He'd read my thoughts.

I blushed.

He continued, "I was spinning my wheels getting nowhere. The wheeler-dealer financier was a mask. The all-knowing guru was a mask. The hermit, protector, and conqueror were masks. Behind each mask, I still controlled everyone around me. Though I had retired from wheeling and dealing, my Warlord nature found new modes to get his just due. He's no easy chap to deal with. Oh, I can kick him out, but—" A Mongolian Warlord spirit shot out from Him and rolled onto the meadow grass, combat style. The spirit loomed up with a demonic wild-eyed expression. "—he returns stronger than ever." The spirit condensed pea size, and My Fool sucked it into His mouth and swallowed. "While you can't ban your nature, you can learn to use it to fulfill your intent."

"So, one's nature and its many faces, serve a purpose."

"Yes." He looked at me pointedly. "What might your facades be?"

"I don't know. Maybe, perfect mother, career woman, savior."

"My facades uphold the image that I am strong." He talked like a game show host. "And the image your facades uphold is?"

"I am good."

"Yes!"

I looked at Him, really looked. There was slipperiness to My Fool. "But you seem in control of your nature, and your image is fading."

"When we are ready to fulfill our intent, we bloom beyond our nature, facades, and image. When that flowering occurs, the authentic self, propelled by Creative Energy, comes into its own. This does not always occur in one embodied experience. For me, I have already blossomed. And now I wilt slowly into a new seed and a new adventure. I linger in the half-world. My identity is seeping back into wholeness, and another 'what if?' "

"So, soon, you will fade away from me?"

"Only as a human in this location."

"You mean you will die?"

"That's another lesson for another day. Today you will learn how your facades, born from your nature, uphold your image. And you will learn how to free yourself from image. This will rocket you into your quintessential self whereupon you can fulfill your intent, this great intent that is a significant thread in life's magnificent tapestry."

My eyes widened. "That's a lot for one day!"

"When one is ready, a lot can happen."

"So, facades uphold our image?"

"Yes. Each facade will try to convince you that their path is the true one, that they alone will lead you to the Promised Land. But their ways are dead ends. I have been there in Mud Lake. And now—you are too."

I crunched my brow. "Is that what the oar is for?"

"I didn't want you to be like I was, up a lake without a paddle," He smiled with whimsy in His eye, ". . . or is that up a creek? Oh well, I never was too bright with words, grammar, handwriting, or spelling. But wisdom . . ." He sighed, "wisdom has always burned in my blood."

"That, I believe," I said. "So what's the paddle for?"

"Here's the hint: you cannot use it to go forward or backward, side to side, up or down."

"What else is there?"

He raised His brows and tossed the oar to me. "It's *your* adventure."

I was always good at catching, and I caught the center of the oar. I understood what He meant about feeling stuck in one's nature, bound to the many faces that projected an image to the world. Yet, I was making progress. I was my own person, finally. I was bucking everyone to take this inner journey, no matter how 'nutty' they deemed me. They couldn't understand why I meditated so often, or worked so radically to change my behavior. Mostly, I absolutely wasn't going to let the facades that supported my sacrificial nature rule my life anymore! Use them to fulfill my intent, yes. But them use me? No more. I was infinitely wiser since I crossed the State Line into myself. And frankly, I looked around scanning the area, there was no sign of a Mud Lake as far as I could see.

I returned my focus to Him.

His eyes penetrated mine. He said, "Aside from this journey, everything you ever did in your life was to uphold an image."

I didn't quite agree that *everything* I did before crossing the State Line was about upholding image, but just when my mouth opened to speak, He blurted, "Think fast now. Uphold the image of an independent, free thinking woman."

I shut my mouth. Anything I said at this point was going to look hypocritical.

He smiled.

Grrrr. I knew He'd read my mind.

He said, "You mustn't appear the hypocrite. Heaven forbid." His smile faded and His eyes grew serious. His intense face seemed to fly right into me, thundering words in my brain. "Your image *has* you. Until you discover this, you cannot accept it. Until you accept it, you cannot release it. Until you release it, you cannot dissolve it. You think you need an image to be loved. You do not."

I knew I didn't need an image to be loved. I was a psychotherapist, and well schooled in such things. Didn't He know I knew that?

My Fool suddenly appeared on a small stage, little yellow wildflowers hugging the base. He arced His arms outwards in a grand gesture against the backdrop of the blue sky. I heard a click.

A spotlight shined on Him. "How we appear to ourselves and the world takes center stage for most people. Intellect supports image. 'I am good because . . . ' 'I am a man because . . . ' Intellect makes decisions to reinforce the image. 'I will clean my house spit-spot and be viewed a good housewife.' Or, 'I will work three jobs to buy a house, so I can be viewed a success.' 'I will memorize facts to look smart or lose ten pounds to look pretty.' Few decisions are ever made that do not serve image."

I kept wanting to defend myself that I really wasn't like that, even though I was. I was bone weary ever trying to prove myself a good mother, wife, friend, therapist, and citizen. Good, good, good, good, good. Still, I'd improved. My image did not currently have me. I was certain.

He went to His knees in prayer pose. "Oh hail ye conscious mind, for you create and guide me. You tell me how I must appear to myself and the world, and convince me that image it is who I am."

Then, like a Shakespearean actor, He stood up with arms outstretched, and bellowed melodramatically:

"Oh conscious mind,
so unfurled.
You give me passage
through this world!

Thank you for keeping me
in the image, I wish to be."

He bowed His head with theatrical sadness, lowering His voice.

"If I brought my hidden self
into the social eye.
I might be deemed worthless;
worthless, I might die."

His head snapped up. His arm flung out. His finger pointed accusingly, voice flaring ire.

"Imagination weaves its tales
from the unconscious mind's abode,
Rubbish that I'm of intrinsic worth,
and that the prince was once a toad!
No, the unconscious realm is dangerous,
home of the insane, the fools, the blind
For I've been told by *intellect*
Reality *is* the Conscious Mind."

He paused and then looked up at me through hooded brows. "Get the point?"

I nodded, very much getting the point. "We often oppress our authentic self because we fear it will get us banned from the social world, and make us feel small against the giant shadow of our peers."

"Yes," He said. "We fear trusting the self behind the image, unlike animals who do not contemplate their instinct to gather food, or to dig a hole, or pick fleas from their peers. They do not defy their natural sense of things. People try."

"Intellect has its place though, doesn't it?"

"Our survival depends on it. Intellect is vital to a world unfolding. Yet, if one wishes to explore what created our reality, intellect can intercede and block us at the pass. Tapping deeper realms of awareness requires quieting conscious thought and putting logic to bed. Sense of life direction, comes from 'sensing,' rather than data analysis. Deeper insight requires fluid thinking. Later, the experiences and insights can be registered, so to speak, by intellect. Yet, if they are defined with finality, much is lost."

I gazed upon the silly stage and the precious body that housed My Fool: violet sweatshirt, white pants, orange socks peaking through the toe holes of His shoes. I think He kind of liked it up there. Here I was, holding a stupid oar, more comfortable being invisible.

I said, "So intellect sustains the outer world, but wisdom is found within?"

He jutted one arm to the air. "Yes!"

Time seemed to blink. Or maybe I did. The stage was gone. He stood before me. "Some things, you just have to experience."

I felt minuscule and immense, and the odd sensation sent me into a panic. I had an urge to race back into the mirror of societal perception, just for awhile, to calm down a bit.

"Run if you wish," He said. "I have run often, but I always wind up running to . . . what I'm running from."

"I will not run." I said, summoning courage. "I will not."

He held His palm a few inches over my forehead. I closed my eyes, reveling in the soothing energy that He sent into my strained brain. My muscles loosened. I exhaled deep and long, allowing my inner barriers to dissolve all the great struggles to be a good wife, and mother, and friend, and housekeeper, and all the other 'ands.' My shoulder blades began sizzling with some strange power, as if I had wings of energy.

His voice melted into me and I never wanted it to stop. "The more you open to Creative Energy unfiltered by your conscious mind, the more you will enhance your current life experience. Many cling to their current reality, fearing change."

He withdrew His hand.

I opened my eyes, feeling more relaxed. "Yes, as a psychotherapist, I see how fear keeps people in painful situations."

He nodded. "Fear pinches Creative Energy's flow, rendering a suffocating life experience. One can literally die barricaded in the self-built house of fearful perceptions. Much of the fear lies in the idea that we won't succeed in the eyes of others. The real self resides deep inside. The real self is the quintessence that wants to flower, but pent up in image, it can't. The secret, silent suffering continues." His voice softened. "Yet, for some reason, that is the experience chosen by that identity. When the time for true change arrives, the authentic self seeded with Pure Creative Energy will crack the hard earth and emerge."

That's what I was trying to do: crack the hard earth and emerge into the outer world as an authentic person, 'box-free.'

He lowered His eyes in a most knowing way that chilled me. "Be brave, Susan."

I gulped and blinked, and He looked normal again, a cheery wise teacher, continuing His lecture. "Another approach spirit-starved people take is the road of addiction."

"I have seen that," I said. "People reach for nourishment by over indulging in alcohol, drugs, food, sex, work, sports, video games, and so much more. Addictions arise from a desperate attempt to fill the emptiness, or negate the pain."

"Yes," He affirmed, "the addiction is the cork on a bottle filled with depression, or panic. If the cork is removed, the addiction broken, depression or panic might surface. 'I am a nun, therefore, I must pray sixteen hours a day, and never have a bad thought.' 'I am a gang member, therefore, I must fight, steal, and kill.' 'I am a housewife, therefore, I must cook and clean, and rear the children, exhausting myself twenty-four hours a day.' 'I am the man of the family; I must provide for them and protect them, no matter what it takes.' "

I said, "That kind of thinking *can* drive a person crazy."

"Once image and the criteria that uphold it are released, relief arrives." He squinted mystically. "What would happen if those people said, 'I am not a nun, gang member, housewife, or man of the family. I'm me. I have a right to be me and flow my true self.' A pool of water that has no flow, stagnates. A person that has no movement—the same. A person locked into the same old boundaries, eventually cannot breathe."

"That's how I feel," I said, "that is why I'm here."

51

"Yes," He said, "you are allowing Creative Energy to expand the very perceptions that cement your current reality. When we increase Creative Energy's flow, perceptions expand and our outer worlds change, creating metamorphic results. Some change is uncomfortable, maybe even seemingly unbearable, yet it can propel us into highly creative life experiences. Sometimes tragedy forces change. The man whose child was murdered, comes to host a show to help put murderers behind bars. The alcoholic who lost his home and family, finally goes into rehabilitation. The business executive who was three times fired shifts allegiance from work to family."

Suddenly it hit me, my tragedy, not as obvious as many. I tapped my oar free hand upon my heart swollen with pain, lips trembling. I felt like I was standing before an Alcoholics Anonymous crowd about to get naked. "I *do* live to uphold my image. I *do* believe I must if I am to be loved. I convinced myself that since I began this journey that I wasn't doing that, but I still am."

He nodded. "Realizing, though a great step, is not doing. Doing requires sinking into the intrinsic flow of your core self."

I closed my eyes and opened my mind, still holding the stupid oar. I stilled, and listened to the sounds around me, hush of wind over tall grass, bees, my own swallowing, my heartbeat, and my slow even breath. I asked for truth beyond all belief systems. I asked to see myself *as I was*, not how I wanted to *believe I was.* Sorrow brewed in my heart, rising to fill my body. I felt caged by goodness, chained to responsibilities not even Superwoman could accomplish. I had to be moral and helpful and clean, and forgiving. I mustn't lie, or hate, or cheat, or be lazy. I mustn't claim glory, or feel pleasure. I must rescue people from their suffering even if it killed me. I must save the world. The world! I thought I was getting beyond all that. Apparently not.

I was yet weighted with grief because I could not execute these tasks perfectly or completely. Even this journey into the inner world was taken to gather the strength to fulfill these tasks. But the truth? I was exhausted from trying. I had the sensation of a gigantic cross around my neck, pulling me down to my knees. My body hurt, trying to carry the burden. Suddenly, heavy cloth swaddled me tightly. I could barely breathe. I snapped my eyes open, panting hard. I *was* my sacrificial nature. I was. But if I consciously used my nature as an instrument to *fulfill my intent,* rather than using it as a cloak to hide behind—I would expose my weaknesses, my fears, and my shame. I didn't know if I was ready to reveal this part of me that I'd always covered.

"Choose and choose quickly," He said, "for the time is now, and it will pass with your next breath."

In my mind, I cried, *But if I release my image, I won't be loved!*

His words turned gentle, like spring rain, "You've made your choice—for now. The puppet is free from responsibility, and the ability to respond. Taking responsibility for one's own reality requires humbleness and *great* courage."

I sank to my knees with the oar, and pressed one hand against my stomach, whimpering, "I failed." Not the duteous student after all.

"You did not fail. You were not ready. Maybe two seconds from now you will be."

I opened one eye and raised a brow. "Do you think?"

He shrugged His shoulders. "It's your decision. I am not your puppeteer." He paused, and smiled. "Well, I'm trying not to be. It would be easier for me if you took control of your own strings."

I would have laughed, but I was too upset by my failure.

He sat next to me. "It is daunting, is it not, to take credit for our own reality and our destiny without berating ourselves. Oh, what a trial to understand what mandate deep within has driven us to experience our current life. Assuming credit for one's reality is more about accepting that we are all one energy and the Creator of our World. And yet, the play must unfold for the tapestry threads to be woven into life's great creation."

I scowled. "The play wearies me, or this play anyway. I *must* broaden my reality by growing beyond the confining shell that houses me. I want to evolve my nature, soften my facades, and forget about image. I want to be an authentic person in this world and blossom into who I am, whatever I am, even if it differs from what others expect of me."

"Then open to the boundless self. See divinity in everything from germs to gerbils to galaxies. Gods and goddesses abound, healers and prophets, sages and seers, all reside in the inner space of your vast . . . infinite . . . self."

My head felt expansive. "We humans do tend to have a finite way of thinking."

"Indeed we do, and yet we are anything but finite. We create the outside world. And we create the cloaks we wear to traverse it. We choose the paths we want to tread. We choose the experiences we want to have, despite impending consequences. We are curious. Earth is our adventure."

"Well, it seems we are doing something wrong. The earth appears extremely out-of-kilter: people blowing each other up, the thinning ozone layer, the rise in addictive behavior, concrete achievement over heart, technology over soul. Is not our world falling apart? How, oh how, I wish I could save it!"

Amusement sparkled in His eye. "The martyr's way. You are quite fond of it, aren't you?"

I swallowed hard, embarrassed that I'd drifted off course so easily, back into the world from which I'd just come. My rambling mind had distracted me. And I knew He knew too. Oh well, image dies hard.

"Image has been the wings of your story. But you are weary of the play, so now—you stop acting. Come swim in the oceans *before* the genesis of all things. Surrender to Creative Energy without definition . . . and *regenerate*."

I blinked. A fat tear rolled down my dusty cheek. I wanted to stop acting and no longer feed my image. But it was so hard, harder than I thought.

"Be kind to yourself." He rose. "The facades that support your image believe they are behaving in your best interest. If you feed your core self rather than your image, you will become stronger and more confident, and thus overshadow the image of what you have *believed* you are."

I sighed, trying to overcome the guilt and shame inside me. I had to believe in my core self, in the hidden one where true beauty lies.

"That's it," He said, in His very special mind reading way.

I rose, still holding my oar, feeling a little better.

Now I wanted to get cleaned up. I glimpsed the tangled mass of hair on my shoulders. I really wanted to brush it. But would that be upholding image? "Does image involve the way we physically present ourselves?"

"It can, if the presentation upholds the image. For instance, a woman needing sexual validation might dress in a way to get it. However, another woman dressed the same, might be expressing her genuine self at that moment. There is nothing wrong with decorating one's body. It is an art form. It is self expression. It is Creative Energy. Why we do, what we do, determines if we are hiding behind image, or not."

"So, fashion has its place."

"Everything has its place, Susan. Releasing image is not for most, nor should it be. Image is not a bad thing, only a thing to be reckoned with if one seeks deep internal change."

I glanced at the cave, thinking of my brush in my knapsack.

When I turned back to Him, He was gone. He seemed so magical. Was He real at all? Maybe I was just insane. In sane. Interesting word. Sane In. Sane Inwardly. Hmm.

I walked into the cave and set down the oar. I picked up my knapsack and opened the top. A gray gem was on my pocket mirror. Not crystalline beautiful gray, no—but rather dark dull gray, ugly really. I wouldn't even call it a gem. I'd call it a pebble.

His voice sounded in my brain, "A gem it is—the Gem of Facade."

My whole pack looked dim, even blurry. Other than the gray gem, I couldn't detect the true form of any object in my purse.

He spoke in my mind, "Facade allows us to cover up what we unconsciously know, motivating us to have life experiences. There would be no earth journey without facade, no repetitive experiences to milk for all their worth."

I wondered why He gave me the Gem of Facade at this juncture. Repetitive experience wearied me. My current goal was to break the repetition and adventure into something different.

I reached into my knapsack to feel for my hairbrush. I felt the bristles and pulled it out.

He said in my mind, "Look nice now. Keep up the image."

Fine! I threw my brush back in my knapsack, annoyed because I really wanted to fix my hair. I wasn't used to it being messy.

His voice sounded in my mind. "Then why listen to *me*?"

"I don't know! You're always right."

"What's right?"

I shrugged my shoulders. "I don't know."

"It is the folly of those who take a mentor, self doubt. The only way you are going to get out of Mud Lake is to listen to that deep down voice, beyond your mind chatter, or the commands of your many facades. If that voice tells you to brush your hair—brush it. Trust you. Not me."

"You disputed me brushing my hair to prove this point, didn't you?"

"Yes. If your inner voice differs from mine, you must follow yours. Even if that voice and mine tell you the same thing, it's not the same thing if you do it by my instruction instead of your own."

"Where are you?"

"The question is, 'Where . . . are . . . *you*?'"

Before I could answer, the cave disappeared, and I was standing knee deep in mud that surrounded me as far as my eyes could see. My knapsack was on one shoulder. The oar was in my hand. I labored in vain to budge one leg.

A spirit girl appeared before me, floating in the air like a ghost. "I'm a good little girl. I work hard to make everyone like me. You mustn't escape Mud Lake by anything immoral."

I strained the muscles in my other leg to take a step. I was cemented.

Next to the Good Little Girl, a spirit woman in a business suit appeared. "I'm an Independent Woman. Do not cry for help. You must free yourself, by yourself, for yourself. We help others. They mustn't help us."

Next to the Independent Woman, a sultry spirit woman appeared. "I'm a Sensuous Woman. I endeavor to make men want me because I find my worth in serving them. Whatever you do, don't get mud on your face!"

I twisted my body trying to turn around. A woman spirit with a hamster-looking face paced back and forth with fidgeting hands.

"Why are you so antsy?" I asked.

She replied almost hysterically, "So much to do, not enough time. Everyone needs me. Have to help them all."

The Good Little Girl added, "And she must do it well!"

The Independent Woman said, "And she must do it well, without crying for help."

The Sensuous Woman added, "And she must look good, while she does it well, without crying for help."

"And she must suffer too." Another voice sounded from beneath me. That was weird. Surfacing from the mud in front of my feet was My Nun's face.

"Oh no," I said, "you again! You, most of all—go away!"

"I am the nature that fuels the others. If you don't want them," said The Nun indignantly, "Come under the mud with me. I am your salvation."

Above me, another voice sounded. "No, I am your salvation. Leave your body and fly away from this earth." I looked up and saw a sweet angelic spirit woman.

A tiger appeared next to her and roared, scaring the winged one into the background. The Tiger said, "Tough it out. Fight. Free yourself from the mud, kick and thrash and push and pull, and never submit, even if it kills you!"

Then they all started talking at once. I didn't know whom to believe. What did My Fool tell me about this? What was it?

I thought He might appear and give me the answer. But He didn't. I thought about using the oar to dig myself out, but I think He said something about that not working, so I didn't waste my energy. Although, then what good was the oar?

Their squawking started to irritate me. "Quiet!" I shouted.

But the more I wanted them quiet, the louder they chattered. The more I wanted them gone, the more visible they became. The more I tried to free myself from the mud, the deeper I sank in. I was in up to my waist, and I feared I'd get in over my head.

Forget about going to hell, I was in hell, probably for crossing the State Line. Probably because there really was a traditional God and He was punishing me. Probably because—"

"That's right," said The Nun, "come to me."

I was sinking. Oh, what was I doing? I was reverting back, major time, to old familiar ground! I was up to my armpits in gunk. "No," I cried, "I am the creator of my own reality, but how do I escape Mud Lake?"

I stopped sinking, but I was more stuck than ever, too rude for the Good Little Girl, too undignified for the Independent Woman, too messy for the Sensuous Lady, too resistant for the Nun, too self absorbed for the Angel, and too frightened for the Tiger.

Minutes passed, hours, days. I felt insane. There was no shutting the facades up or escaping Mud Lake! I was hungrier, thirstier, and more soul-starved than ever before. Weeks passed. I endured the incessant chatter of my facades by concentrating on sunshine and rainbows and butterflies. But after awhile, even that didn't work. No physical person had ever haunted me worse than I was haunting myself, my awful horrendous self! Those in the outside world probably viewed me as high strung, nervous, and panicky.

Months passed. The sun rose and set more times than I could count. I cried. I screamed. I yelled profanities. I meditated, fantasized, and prayed; I called for anything in creation that could help me.

Then I gave up.

Those in the outside world would have viewed me as depressed, tired, and low on spirit, going through the motions with no joy inside.

Many people lived this way, going through the motions, getting nowhere, a zombie upholding facade, while the real self sank into oblivion.

There was no escaping Mud Lake. The oar was useless. My Fool must have been toying with me, hinting its purpose. I was miserable, so miserable.

If success wasn't about making money, or appearing sexy, or being perfect, then how could I feel good about myself? Everywhere I looked, someone was expecting me to be those things, mostly—

me. If I gave up the facades, what would be left? Nothing maybe. And that scared me most of all. If I stripped away the good wife, perfect mom, great therapist, sexy woman, nun, angel, and good little girl—then what was I? Who was I?

I realized then that the facades continued chattering, because I hadn't really been willing to release them. Yet, in retaining them, I was only half-alive. No wonder few people took this journey. The term, "Ignorance is bliss" took on a whole new meaning.

I recalled His words, *Choose and choose quickly, for the moment is now. With the next breath, it will be gone.*

My selves said in unison, "You'll perish, if you don't emanate through one of us!"

My conviction set in. "No, I am perishing because I emanate through all of you. Together you create an image that is impossible for me to uphold. I lose myself to the image, and this I can no longer bear!"

"We are you!"

"You are my shell."

I realized I had chosen. I chose exposure, risking shame, guilt, terror. Whoever I was, whatever I was, I wanted to become that, no longer oppressed by the facades that upheld an image like a static picture, like a caterpillar stuck in its cocoon.

My eyes slid shut in deep view of the inner world. "Who am I?" I murmured. Calmness overcame me. I answered myself. "I am Creative Energy. The roles I play are manufactured by my perception of reality. I widen my perception now, seeing more while also embracing the infinitesimal. I am the Pure Creative Energy that permeates everything, the pebble, the sea, the Universe, molecules, sounds, colors, emotions, and concepts of being." Concentrating on this, I moved into dynamic stillness. My body vibrated fluid energy, absorbing image and the pillars of facade. Panoramic beauty held in a dot.

Mahler's *Symphony No. 2, Resurrection*, filled the air. I could hear it naturally! Not in my head, and not through headphones. Maybe music did play always, everywhere, as My Fool had insinuated. Maybe we just couldn't hear it over the din of surface world chatter. I had a visionary experience, a story of my human journey.

I was nailed to a cross of my own making. Centuries had weathered my pallid face. My deep ancient wounds made pain eternal. Getting off this cross, turned urgent.

With my mind, I moved into the single point that threaded my every life experience in the theme of 'martyr.' I saw it then, this experience I kept trying to have, but forfeited to a life of martyrdom, many times over. It was the experience of shining my true self out into the world as an authentic being, allowing the Creative Life Force to pulse through me, unimpeded by perception. I wanted to impart the wisdom that flowed through me, sing it like a great song, the greatest song on earth. I wanted to sing it loud, proud, and be unshaken by criticism. Reception of my song was not the thing. The thing was to simply sing it.

The old martyr-victim story had been milked dry. I could no longer bear the ancient agony, the giant rage, the deep hatred, the unfathomable sorrow of this worn theme. Now I would begin to experience the world in a whole new way, or maybe a whole new world.

I chanted, "I am Creative Energy." I became a white-hot flame that forged a tunnel, deeper, deeper, deeper to somewhere I did not know. Energy intensified. My body quaked. My head felt big. My body too. My skin felt afire. The mud loosened around me. I felt my facades break free and transform like caterpillars that had found wings.

I thought I might dissolve, but instead I seemed to erupt and spill out in all directions. I heard popping sounds. The nails that held me to the cross burst out of my skin and I knew now that the old wounds could finally begin to heal.

I fell off the cross, sobbing with relief. I forgave myself, unenslaved myself. My facades no longer led the way. It was now, I who led the way, at least for now, at least for once. Tears streaked my face. The weight of the world's expectations had been lifted from my broken shoulders. I no longer had to be a good little girl, a perfect mom, a dutiful wife, a sexy woman, a super-human therapist, a successful writer. I didn't have to be a martyr anymore. I had shaken the 'habit.'

Who I was no longer counted. My image meant nothing. All

that mattered was that I shined Creative Energy from my deepest being. Period. Whatever else I might say or do, it would all be okay because an unconditional lovingness coursed through me.

My kids would be okay, because I loved them. My husband would be okay, because I loved him. I would be okay, because I loved me. The house could stay messy. I could twiddle my thumbs. I could go to Africa. I could stand on my head in a convent. I could yodel from rooftops. I could be a genuine human being, free from all the heavy cloaks the world would have me wear. Who would have thought that the solution to my burdens was as elementary as—shed them. I felt brilliantly awakened.

Time for you to awaken too. Release your binding self-image and join me in this magical world where you paint the picture of your life, blotting this and that, adding that and this, never forgetting that you are the painter, and the picture is only a picture, a creation of yours. Oh, behold the true Creator. Behold!

If you can't join me yet, I bet I know where you are. Mud Lake, right? If you seek escape, *if* you do, save yourself the struggle of battling the many selves within you. The battle will be eternal and fruitless until you surrender to the Whole of Creation, which is YOU. Summon Creative Energy to bring the deep authentic you to the surface and your surface selves to the deep. Masks pale in Creative Energy. More and more, you experience yourself as *all that is*.

Have you the bravery to let your life change? Have you the courage to let *yourself* change? Heaven on earth awaits. You'll spread your arms like expansive wings and shout with elation. "Ain't—Life—Great!"

Take a moment this day to meditate with classical or new age music. Or with some form of nature, physical or imagined. Or simply give yourself over to the whisperings of the authentic self crying to be free. If you succeed in surrendering your small self to your great self, I'll see you soon in a very . . . special . . . place.

In The Zone
"There's no place like home, and home is no place."

GEM #4 POLYPHONY

I heard clapping. I opened my eyes, knapsack on back, oar still in hand. I hovered in a crystal-clear chasm. Around me, breathtaking terrains blended into one, a collage of mountains in oceans, oceans in skies, skies in forests, forests in deserts. Patterns were boldly defined, yet indefinable. Colors were brilliant, yet unlike any hues I'd ever seen. My skin felt soda water effervescent. Vitality permeated by being.

"Welcome to The Zone." My Fool appeared beside me, brown eyes twinkling the secrets of heaven and earth, headphones in place. "Open your hand, grasshopper," He said, imitating Cain's master on the Kung Fu television series.

I opened my hand.

He dropped a clear crystal gem in my palm. "This is the Gem of Polyphony. Numerous realities co-exist in everyone and everything, and can be consciously experienced simultaneously."

My eyes grew big. "Really?"

He slid His palm against the back of my hand and curled my fingers around the gem. The gem expanded as a growing spiritual entity, becoming less dense until it superimposed over me. I inhaled the cool air of its aura that seemed to condense into a liquid, replenishing every thirsty particle of my being. I exhaled, feeling most insightful.

His voice flowed thick, slow, colorfully into my essence. "There is no place like home, and home is no place."

I looked around at the beauteous collage. "Home?"

"Yes, the place you can hang your hat and put up your feet. You know . . . home."

"I'm not sure I can call this home, but I could call it heaven." I inhaled a slow deep breath, stretching my arms overhead. I exhaled with reverence, arcing my arms downward to rest at my sides. "I feel exalted, cleansed, like I've been reborn."

"You will feel more real here than anywhere on the planet."

"Where *is* this Zone exactly?"

Fluid warmth carried His voice. "It is the center of everyone's reality beyond their identity and their drama. And yet the awareness of their drama is not forgotten, nor has it disappeared. It is the juggler who steps away from the life he associates with his identity, and finds the balls still fly through the air in perfect harmony. It is the broken-hearted working mother swallowed by the sorrow of betrayal, who steps away from her role and her pain, only to find herself timeless and significant. She is the dazzling Universe and all of its components that no earth drama or identity can diminish."

I looked around. I was surrounded by clarity, but the far far distance was blurred.

"That's where you've been," He said. "Don't gaze out there too long or you'll go there, and you've worked too hard to get here."

"Does one typically enter The Zone following a great feat?"

"It is a state of being arrived at through various means: a great feat, becoming so still that the reality of small-world thinking moves on without you, riding pain to the outer limits of one's awareness, or consciously moving one's self into *The All*. Sometimes, the dream worlds are the transport, or the slightest shift in focus from one's own troubles to the fluffy squirrel jumping from tree to tree. All these require expanding beyond self-image."

With energy charged fingers, I rubbed my forehead. "Moving beyond my self-image was the *hardest* thing I've *ever* done."

His hand touched my shoulder, warmth soothing me to the bone. "I don't want to bust your bubble, but as I am a bubble buster, I must be true. Be prepared. Getting to The Zone is one feat; staying is another. Since we are still aware of our identity, yet at the same time of our oneness with all existence—maintaining balance can be tricky. However, it is possible to live polyphonically, experiencing mundane life while also emanating from The Zone. You can for instance, simultaneously take your daughter to dance lessons, experience your true connection with her, observe the grand earth story, and the Creative Energy outside time and space. You feel yourself as *The All*, and yet as the identity of Susan."

"So, we needn't shift our focus back and forth from surface and depth. All levels can be experienced concurrently?"

"Yes, Susan. It is a matter of practice. Polyphonic awareness generates a smoother living experience. For example: You are in a store. You got the last cart. While you are looking at vitamins, another woman sneakily removes what's in your cart and strolls away with it. You say angrily, 'Excuse me, that is *my* cart!' You are simultaneously aware that your good little girl self is uncomfortable, and that is why your heart pounds. Your wise self nods approvingly, knowing what a coup it is for you to express the anger you usually repress, and that is why you smile inside. Your holistic self sees you are fulfilling part of your life intent, and that is why behind the pounding heart, and inner smile, you are quiet inside. Your ascended self realizes this is an experience you created to enact a drama that would take you on an adventure, and that is why you feel metaphorical wings on your back. This, all in one blink, can prove most beautiful and satisfying."

The image of a great orchestra came to mind. "So, living polyphonically is like hearing each instrument play its own melodic line of music, while also hearing the whole symphony."

He nodded with a smile. "It is about living life from a centered point of view, yet experiencing all that emanates around you."

It sounded so beautiful. I just doubted I could do it.

"Take heart," He said, "if you should fall from the center and see, think, and feel, only what your image ordains."

My face sagged. I began to fade.

He pressed His palm firmly against my forehead. "Hold on. You worked hard to reach The Zone. Don't run off yet."

My mind brightened, defining the edges of my thought. Steady now . . . steady. Balance returned. I sighed with relief, realizing how easily this centeredness could be lost.

He took the oar from me, rocking back to one foot like an old baseball pro, and hurled it, spinning at top speed, giving the illusion of a circle rocketing into the distant blurriness. The oar disappeared, gobbled up in the distortion. He brushed His palms past each other several times for a job well done. "You didn't need that anymore."

I stared in a stupor at where the oar disappeared, ever amazed at how events occurred in the inner world. "What was the oar for anyway?"

"Nothing. Yet, if you didn't possess such a prop, you would have wasted months wanting it, thinking it would help you take direction. At best it would have only helped you create a new facade with a false sense of direction. But, since you had the oar, and realized it wouldn't get you anywhere, you surrendered that notion quickly."

"So, using props like taking a trip or college course, having a baby or an affair, getting a new hairdo or a car, to solve an internal conflict—is only a temporary fix. The conflict stems from inside us, therefore resolution is found within, not without."

"Yes. The outer world slips and slides. Mirages abound. The journey within leads us to the core of all things. Yet, most people do not go that way. The first instinct when hurt is to slip a facade in place and serve one's nature. The warrior might appear stoical, shooting metaphorical arrows at others to distract from his own pain. The martyr might appear fine, pretending nonexistence in a metaphorical cave, comfortable in her pain. Such cloaking, however, yields only temporary relief. Meanwhile the heart, deep down remains discontent."

I cocked my head. "The journey within also leads us to encounter our facades, like when I was in Mud Lake."

"And what did you do to get unstuck?"

"I journeyed deeper. Those facades are culprits."

"And yet, what would we do without them?"

"Probably celebrate!"

"No, Susan. You wouldn't. Your facades are the roles you think you are, sometimes blending, sometimes conflicting, but always the players that create your personality, necessary to exact the plot in your own great story. Sometimes in the story, we cry for change.

It is then we can find The Zone, that inner balance that deepens our awareness. Seeing deeply, allows us to dissolve our image, and consciously use our nature to enrich our lives. For me, that means laying down the sword and blending into the collective. For you, it means embracing the sword, standing your ground, and singing your song. As awareness expands, it becomes easier to seize control of your reality."

My mind flashed upon my many facades from Mud Lake. "It's so hard to emanate energy without getting lost in a role. I mean when I am with my children, I think of myself as their devoted mother. When I am with a client, I think of myself as a dedicated psychotherapist. How does one who is in a role not become the role? I want to emanate from my core self."

My head jolted back. Tiny cartoon grasshoppers were hopping out of My Fool's mouth, then vanished in the air with a twinkle. I was glad they vanished, because cartoon or not, I didn't want them landing on me. Grasshoppers kind of scared me.

"You shine *through* the roles, Susan. The roles are there, but *who you are* shines through them. The roles take on facades' power only when you need to feel important. Don't you see the irony?"

"About Grasshoppers?"

"About importance. We do not actually need facades to realize our importance. All identities are equally significant, regardless of societal judgment or how history presents. Yet, we are all judged—especially those who stand alone adhering to the rhythm deep within their being, rather than from the social current pulling strong all around them. These soloists, or 'fools on the hill' are capable of seeing the overview that everyone is on a personal mission that uniquely shapes them. Each shape is a puzzle piece essential for the whole earth picture to be complete, a picture that is continuously moving and becoming more than it was. They see the intrinsic worth in everything, even garbage, even sewage, and the song they sing is polyphonic."

"So, people who live in facade seek significance in their social reality. But if they embrace their significance—" I stopped short. For some reason I had a bout of insecurity, perhaps a bit of trouble embracing my significance. A ghost-like monster loomed behind me. I felt myself fading again, wavering, almost falling.

"Shoo!" My Fool said to it, but it didn't go away. He said to me, "Keep focus. Behold your significance and the 'monsters' will fade away." His eyes twinkled. The twinkles shot out, forming into those cartoon grasshoppers. They blasted around my face. I winced. They disappeared, and I almost did too. Staying in The Zone was hard!

"I am significant," I murmured to myself to deepen my focus. And my monster—the monster of insecurity, vanished.

A halo of stars appeared above My Fool's head. As He spoke they glowed brighter, even sparkling sometimes. "All 'beings' are significant, and always have been. In fact, if they tried not to be, they still would be. Significance permeates everything. It courses through the bloodstream, sending millions of little universes through the body. It courses through the mind stream that sends the stars in motion across the sky. It courses through the heart stream that produces music and poetry and mathematical beauty. Every 'being' possesses all this. Open your eyes! Who is not significant? Who does not add to the collage of adventure we created for the benefit of our own experience? *Significance is Intrinsic.* Yet, to have experiences we perform the tragic play and put many through the ringer, including ourselves, to attain what we already possess. When the experience is finished, we remember who we are. And yet, ironically, it is the 'not knowing' that gives our lives meaning."

Strangely enough, I began to see it His way. The glaring bully, pummeling the meek to win the title of 'superior' in the pecking order game. The housewife, scrubbing and cleaning the house until her back breaks, all to get the proverbial pat on the shoulder. When all the while, they are both significant as is, and needn't do anything to attain it. Yet what kind of story could be had if we all knew that from the 'get go?'

I smiled, balanced in The Zone, once more. "We create huge dramas, getting huffy, puffy, and emotional, when all along, behind the play, we are each, already, constantly—infinitely beautiful. It is like someone yelling their head off, or crying their guts out because they don't have wings on their back, when they actually do. They just can't see them."

His body started emanating light rays. "And that applies to you too. But because you don't believe you have wings on your back, your facades rise to a rescue you don't really need, promising you what you already possess."

I whispered to myself. "I possess everything." Rays of light burst from my fingertips. I gasped, staring at my hands as if they weren't my own.

His body emanated even brighter rays. "You shine the moon. You are the moon. Is it better to be a lawyer? A doctor? A politician?"

My head felt open, imparting rays of pleasant intensity.

He said, "You shine the sun. You are the sun. Could a Pulitzer Prize be more rewarding?"

My heart fluttered, and it seemed a thousand butterflies burst into my head whispering answers to life's most daring questions. I closed my eyes. Quietly I murmured, "I know everything without having to know anything."

"Ah," He said, "and would you rather have a Ph.D.?"

I opened my eyes and smiled. "I get it. Even our facades are beloved, birthed by Creative Energy, designed to create a life story. Curiosity generates direction. The desire to experience promotes action. The arrow is shot. Consequences follow. A story will be had. When we tire of those consequences, we will want to change the direction, the story." I gave a brisk sigh. "That's the hard part."

"Yes, but less hard than staying the same. When I release my perceived enemies knowing they are me, the Mongolian Warlord rises and roars. 'Mow them down! Take control!' Or if no one is getting the point of my brilliant wisdom, the Guru in me rises and says, 'To hell with them. They are ignorant!' "

I laughed. His animated facial expressions were quite entertaining.

He shrugged His shoulders. "In these cases, I'm using Creative Energy to experience winning by allowing my facades to direct Creative Energy. If I instead allow Creative Energy to flow, unimpeded by my facades, the story changes. My experience exceeds anything my facades could muster. True brilliant works of art, music, science, and humanitarian endeavor arise this way, because

Creative Energy, flowing unimpeded, opens one to the power of the whole Universe. Extraordinary experiences occur when we release the directives we give ourselves, or the directives others give us." His whole body emanated brilliant light rays.

Mine did not. Only my head and hands emanated light. "Yes," I said, "I get it." My brows shot up. "Facade is who we *think* we are, and Creative Energy is who we *really* are." At last, my whole body glowed light.

"Well put!" He nodded approvingly. "Facade gives the illusion that you are significant and safe. But all facades lead to dead ends in their search for significance, like reaching the tip of a tree limb. Transcending facades leads one to experience the whole tree. Imagine how the feeling of safety grows when one's whole identity is not cast into one limb that can be snapped with a single blow. When you begin to realize that you are the whole tree, it's easier to let leaves fall and let branches break, knowing that new ones will sprout. The need to salvage a facade at any cost—diminishes."

I stretched my arms outward once again, inhaling deeply ions of energy that charged my body. When I exhaled, I whispered, "There's no place like home, and home is no place."

He said, "If anyone were to gaze upon you now, they'd be so taken with your sparkle and shine, they would bow. This is the glow people seek through outer world achievement. As you can see, the outer world has zero to do with *this* achievement. You have come home to the seat of Creative Energy where there is clarity and the ability to see life polyphonically. You are in The Zone!"

"I understand." I nodded reverently. "Our facades support an image that we are terrified to release. This self-image has become a veneer we hide behind. We fear that beneath the veneer, we might find unimportance. But in fact, we discover the opposite, importance beyond comprehension."

"Precisely. You can see how the world appears from here: people fighting each other for a place in the sun, competing for attention, winning a mate, corporate battles, civil wars, world unrest— all for what can be achieved by shifting focus from the outer world to the inner world."

"I wish we could save them." Again, I started to fade, my light rays retreating. So *hard* to stay balanced.

"They do not need saving. Everyone's experience is a gift, precious and packed with treasure. It is the way it is supposed to be."

"I hear what you are saying, but sometimes it is difficult to look at all the hardship in the world and see the advantage of living."

"The Earth Story and all its facades, the impression of separation, and the struggle to feel important—are profound experiences. Every identity experiences reward and loss, rage and peace. Time to time, some wish the current Earth Story would end and peace on earth would prevail. But without conflict, there is only staleness. Without labor, a baby cannot be born. Without struggle, a flower cannot break ground, nor experience blooming. Some wish to escape the Earth Story, but deep down, if that were their wish, they wouldn't be here in the first place. The rules collectively accepted by earth consciousness are created by us to have an experience. When your story has been milked for all it is worth, and your earth journey has been brought to balance, one's being will exit the Earth Story the way it entered, through the vibration of Eleven. I call it Highway Eleven."

I cocked my head. "Highway Eleven?"

"Highway Eleven is the vibration that a being moves into when entering earth. It is where a being creates the wardrobe of identities it will wear in the earth journey. These identities are created with master intents and sub-intents, mandates and sub-mandates, and references (particular genetics, propensities, and personality traits) needed to fulfill multitudes of adventures in various embodiments."

"So in a way, we, meaning Creative Energy, grand design ourselves to experience earth."

"We grand design that too."

I shook my head in an effort to comprehend. "We grand design earth?"

"We grand design everything."

His words were rather mind blowing, and I had to continually stretch my boundaries to behold His insights.

"Highway Eleven," He continued, "is the bow from where the arrow is shot, and a 'being' begins its earth journey. It is also here that the journey ends—where in exiting earth, all the identities that a being has worn, are hung up for entering beings to reassemble new identities. Highway Eleven is my current destination."

"That is why you seem sort of transparent, isn't it?"

"Yes," He said. "It is a path open to those who are ready to cash in their round trip ticket that has enabled the experience of perceiving separation, time, and space with an identity. The ticket is worn and crumpled, but never lost. Misplaced from time to time, but never gone. The vibration of Highway Eleven is eternally bonded to all."

The white light around His body turned into rainbow ripples that encompassed me. He sighed hard. "I have played out earth's themes, with its many possibilities. My master intent is near complete. Highway Eleven beckons."

"If you leave, will I ever see you again?"

"What is I? What is you? We were never really apart, so we can never be separated. However, the entity Susan may or may not experience the me you have known. This would depend on your ability to multi-dimensionally connect."

"Where do you, as a being, go after Highway Eleven?"

"I can remain there as a watcher, an observer without involvement to further expand awareness. Or, I can experience worlds not of earth, entering a different vibration, for example, Highway Seven. Or, I can complete dissolution of perceived separation and shift focus from a 'being' to Pure Creative Energy beyond time and space. We are all always everywhere. Again, it is a matter of focus."

I felt my essence expanding. "What will you choose?"

His eyebrows raised. "We shall see."

The radiance around me thickened. Rainbow ripples moved out from me as they did Him. I had a vision. A child inside me rose, standing tall with outstretched hands. Her name was Liberty. "My heart is free!" she cried. She seemed alive in me. I loved her. She wasn't unruly as children can be. She was my joy.

I jolted. In the far far distance, a blurry silhouette of a young human on hands and knees crawled closer to us. I closed my eyes, looking inward and sighed. Was that a part of me coming home? Was this the child that in my vision just rose within me?

His arms flung out. "Yes! Ain't—Life—Great!"

I smiled. "You are reading my mind again."

"I *am* you. You *are* me. We *are* life, multidimensional, never ending, always happening, ever creating. Life delivers beauty, joy, surprise, and the seed for the next 'what if.' Each finale leads to a new beginning. Mahler's *Symphony No. 8* evokes words in me. "Remember, how to remember. Creative Energy is in all, of all, and all. Flow it. Become it. Behold new creation!"

He exhaled.

I inhaled.

His arms lowered.

Mine rose in slow motion.

He became still and quiet.

My body vibrated, feeling afire!

I opened my eyes. "There are no facades in The Zone."

"No," He replied, "You released them. That's why you're here. That's why I'm here."

"How come no one else is here?"

"Oh, they come from time to time, but The Zone is not heavily populated, for it requires a balanced state of mind not colored with a belief system."

"Don't you get lonely?" My heart sank, longing to share this splendor with others.

He said, "Only for the Infinite Oneness I once knew."

I nodded. "Me too."

Tears gathered in my eyes. I had a mental picture of another world where unity was commonplace. Oh, not the Infinite Oneness, but a place where the voices of choral chanting manifested events. Weird.

Quite suddenly, He disappeared.

I got scared, and a gut-wrenching loneliness grabbed me.

I began falling in slow motion down a clear tube. I glimpsed all the people that were ever in my life, but they seemed fake, like robots in a dead world. It was like, only I existed. Suddenly, I decided I hated the feeling. I panicked. I screamed. No one could hear me.

I tried to touch the outer world on the way down, but no one could feel me. I stared right at them, but they could not see me.

Suffice it to say, I'd fallen out of The Zone.

If you ever get in The Zone, take heart if you fall out. Humans often fall. It is the way it is supposed to be. Whether you are out of it trying to get in, or in it and have fallen—touch your face like a mother's hand on her newborn infant. Charge yourself with faith in life. Feel a trillion stars entering the pores of your skin, filling your brain with potions of Creative Energy. Then release fear, and view the fall as another experience to create another chapter in your life, another snowflake falling through the winter sky. If your goal is to live polyphonically, then each experience is a step to help you climb back into The Zone. Each time you fall, you'll return to The Zone quicker. Each time you return to The Zone, it will be easier to remain longer and live life polyphonically. The large self can experience the synchronistic symphony while the small self lives the drama of an identity separate from others.

Embrace your experience outside The Zone. Drink it in. Live it fully. Then one day you will not be a small self in a big world. You will be a big self in a limitless world. I might view you driving to work in your car, shopping for groceries, or in line at the bank. But I'll know that you're not really driving, shopping, or banking. You are trying to come alive, by DRIVING . . . SHOPPING . . . and BANKING.

The only way to come into The Zone is to BE HERE NOW, transcending individual viewpoint, and not be lost in what you are doing, or preoccupied with where you are going. Instead, be aware of the *way* you are doing what you are doing, and where you are now, within. Where is your head? Where is your heart? In the particle? Or the whole? Maybe both? Practice experiencing both at once, seeing the small and large picture without analyzing, defining, or judging. Enter The Zone. See you there!

The Desert of Loneliness
Make your own way, and your way will be made."

GEM#5 INDEPENDENCE

I hit bottom. My behind plopped on a gray sand dune. A cloud of granules engulfed my body. My Fool was sitting next to me, shaking the sand from His hair. His body appeared more dense than usual.

Sand clung to my tongue. Yuck. I have got to learn to keep my mouth shut. I let my mouth fill with saliva, and spit out the grains the best I could. Not lady-like I know, but maintaining image was no longer a goal.

I wiped renegade granules off my tongue, and looked to Him. "What happened?"

"Our loneliness took hold." He removed the Walkman from His pants waist and blew off the sand.

"Where are we?"

He replaced the Walkman with great care, more concerned about it than our seeming dilemma. "Where else, but the Desert of Loneliness."

"So, you've been here before."

"Frequently."

I scanned the miles of drab sand under somber gray skies. "Now what?"

"Now? What?" He rose and brushed sand off His lips. "I go my way. You go yours. At least for now."

I gasped. "Why? I don't want to be alone here!"

"You'll be fine."

"Why do you want to leave me?"

"You make me feel—more than I wish."

"But—"

"It's not becoming to the Warlord in me."

"But—"

"I keep him in check, but he's not obsolete."

His stoical attitude shocked me. I was used to Him being above all this, but then I remembered, He was still the half man, and this was His man half, and probably why His body seemed more dense.

I said bravely, "Then I challenge you to be vulnerable. I believe that is good for you."

His eyes flashed something dark and kingly.

I gulped. "I mean, you *chose* to be with me."

His face softened. "There is an old wound that needs tending. I need time alone to prepare."

"I don't want to be alone in this desolate place."

"You never are. Loneliness is an illusion."

"Still, the feeling is—" I stood and surveyed the landscape. Barren gray sand waves gave way to flat sand seas, without a trace of civilization as far as my eye could see, "—overwhelming."

The spot on the dune where I was standing collapsed under my feet. I shrieked, sliding down fast. Sand flew in my mouth again, choking me. Gravity ripped away my knapsack. I landed at the bottom, and coughed into my lap, pushing grit out of my throat. Assaulted by a sand dune. A first for me.

My knee gaped through the even now bigger hole in my jeans. My other knee peeked through fragile threads to join its mate. The fabric on my shirt was wearing thin and dotted with little holes near the hemline. I wanted to cover up with something else, but I had a scary sense clothing was antithetical to my inner world goals. Vulnerability? Oh yes, I could relate to my wizened teacher. The humiliation. The fear.

He shuffled down on His feet, grabbed my pack, and stopped at my side.

I spit out more sand and looked up at Him through a billow of gray dust. I felt like a bad girl. "How come you didn't fall?"

"I have practiced balance more than you. I came here for a reason, to get hold of something. You just came, so you are unsteady."

"Oh," I conceded, pouting.

He tossed the knapsack on my lap. "I wouldn't want you to lose all those gems I've been giving you."

"I'm giving you a gem too, aren't I?"

The dark kingly thing came over Him again. He nodded. We didn't say what the gem was that I was giving Him, but we both knew it was sensitivity, and it was shaped like the human heart—. the thing I think, He was trying to experience fully to complete His earth adventure.

"Come," He said, turning around, "let's walk."

I was relieved that I was allowed to tag along. I rose, slung my pack over my shoulder, aggravating the bruise I received from the fall. Trekking the inner world could be painful. People often get unexplained aches and pains, perhaps this was partially why. We walked side by side over soft fine sand, so deep, it filled my hiking shoes. "Tell me about this place."

I heard Vaughn Williams' Symphony, *The Lark Ascending*, escaping the headphones, lending background music to His voice. "You are here because you feel alienated. You are no longer content to interact with people's facades. You crave deeper connection. But everywhere you go, you see people living in facade, for societies in general praise conformity, and chastise those who differ or behave unconventionally. Your social mask is off. This threatens those who wear the mask, and believe they *are* the mask. One who wears a narcissistic mask might believe she is truly the greatest woman on earth. One who wears the victim mask might truly believe the whole world conspires against him. To them, an authentic person who wears no mask might be viewed as idiotic and maybe untouchable. Hence loneliness."

"So what do I do?"

"The Desert of Loneliness has much to offer. You might want to stay awhile."

"I don't want to stay here."

"Then shift focus and return to The Zone. However, remaining in The Zone for longer periods requires inner world exploration. Understanding the many facets of yourself strengthens polyphonic sight. If you have never heard the clarinet, you will not recognize it in the symphony."

My eyes glistened. I felt like I was talking to the wisest man, or half man on earth. "Okay, what does loneliness have to offer?"

"Independence, dear Susan . . . independence."

"Oh, I get it. I can be free from upholding my image, which is pretty draining."

"Yes, but there is another prize. As you are discovering, a primary mandate in the identity of Susan involves liberation from the martyr-victim pattern with the intent of experiencing an unmasked reality. To that end, you need references such as, 'The world needs saving. I must save the world through self-sacrifice. Sacrifice means I am spiritual, worthy, and beloved by a higher power. Trying to save everyone is exhausting, and often gets me victimized. I need protection. I need a warrior to protect me, but warriors haven't protected me. I must protect myself. I must save myself. Can I?' "

I didn't realize I was holding my breath. With apple cheeks, I sighed loudly. He had me pegged. "So, independence is a mandate that will help me fulfill my intent?"

"It will help you fulfill *your* intent. Everyone's intent, mandate, and references are slightly if not vastly different. For me, I cannot spell. That inability is necessary. It propelled me to journey off the beaten path where I made my fortune young. This fed my Red-eyed Power Monger and nearly destroyed me. And that drove me to retire early to tend my flailing family and take the journey 'within' that led me to The Zone, and soon Highway Eleven."

I sighed hard. "People's stories are really quite beautiful. Are these stories, or shall I say intents, fulfilled before we die?"

"Some are. However, the journey of a 'being' always is. Even as bodies dissolve into the earth, the master intent continues to call for fulfillment. Intents are like trees. The trunk is the master intent for the whole earth adventure. Branches are lifetimes of sub-intents Leaves, are sub sub-intents in a life. These sub sub-intents are no less magnificent than the master intent, for indeed the smallest sub-intent is necessary for fulfillment of the master intent."

A whizzing noise sounded above me. Looking up, I was more than a little startled to see an enormous book falling from the gray sky, thundering toward our heads. I jumped back, just in case I was the target. The immense book slammed on the sandy desert floor between us, kicking up dust and a few small pebbles. The deep blue hardback was as long as my body and thick to my waist! The title read *The Adventures of a Being on Earth.*

He reached over and brushed off a bit of dust from the cover. I noticed then that the blue was dotted with miniscule star clusters.

"This book seems old," I said.

"I summoned it to further demonstrate intent, mandate, and earth life."

"Oh," I replied, eager to peek inside.

"Open it," He said.

I opened the giant cover, clumsily. The table of contents listed, Book One, Book Two, into the hundreds. As I scanned down, the page kept getting longer.

"This is weird," I said.

"Multi-level dimensions are elusive to the human mind. My attempts to show or explain anything are but simplifications because language is insufficient."

"What's up with these hundreds of books within a book?"

"In the concept of time, each book, which may require multiple embodiments, represents a theme such as: authoritarian, healer, wanderer, isolationist, victim, martyr, or combinations thereof. Each chapter represents an embodiment, or lifetime. Look at Book One. What does it say?"

I read the words. "The Martyr."

"This book alone might require many embodiments to explore. Go to the first chapter."

I turned the page, and the first chapter title read, "The Experiences of a Martyr as a Nun."

He grazed His fingers along the page. "Each chapter is a lifetime. Subsequent chapters would explore being a martyr in different ways under different circumstances. Chapter Two might read, "The Experiences of a Martyr as a Soldier." Chapter Three might read, "The Experiences of Martyr as a Mother." Of course, each book and chapter is filled with multiple sub-intents, mandates, and references. When a book or theme is finished, one might move onto a new theme, such as 'The Authoritarian.' This would be the next book in the Big Book. All the books completed are a 'being's' experience of the Great Earth Adventure."

"Whose book is this?"

He raised a brow. "Why, it's yours."

I gasped. "Mine! But it looks finished."

"Perceptions. In 'no time,' all is already written, though ever changing. What appears as Book One for you, might actually be Book One Hundred. Your perceptions reflect your point of focus, which is currently 'the martyr.' Therefore, it might seem to you that a martyr is all you've ever been."

"I want to read it!"

"Susan, my dear, you wrote it."

"I want to read it anyway."

"Then, read."

"I focused on the words in Book One, Chapter One. My eyes scrolled to the first sentence. '*Misty Energy condensed into the belly of . . . of . . .*' Words kept changing as I tried to read. I glared at Him, frustrated. "Why can't I read it?"

"The meanings are inner spatial, and you are trying to read with physical eyes. Everything you do each second changes the past and future. Change is constant."

"But I want to review the journey of my being."

The book sank into the earth in a ghostly fashion. And there it went, a detailed record of a being's adventure on earth. Mine.

"No!" I groused, "I want my book back."

He said, "Susan, you can travel into any chapter of your book anytime by moving deep within, and touching Creative Energy unfiltered by conscious perception. This is what you did shortly after crossing The State Line, and when you left Mud Lake. In the flashes of those moments, you will *see* and you will *know*."

"You mean, we can time travel in our own story?"

"Yes."

"That is exciting, but," I frowned, "seeing the Book of Me sink into the earth, saddens me."

"That is because you are lonely for yourself. We all are, but the seekers and the deep thinkers feel it most. Each 'being' is vast, yet only parts of 'be ing' . . . are remembered. This discombobulates the seekers. We want to connect the dots, yearning to figure out who we are and why we are. We desire to understand the people around us. How do they fit in?"

"Speaking of that," I said, "how do other people figure into our book? Everyone I know must be in mine, so am I in theirs?"

"Yes, but everyone is the main character in their own story."

"Do the characters gather repeatedly to play out themes that require multiple embodiments?"

"There is that," He said. "Remember, there is really everything. I am only sharing what I have experienced thus far. My hope is that you will pursue your own adventure and find your own in-sights."

"I know, but please tell me more about what *you* have found."

"Very well. We can attract the same players to flame the fire, stir the pot, or calm the waters. We form ongoing relationships with these players whom we might love, hate, or not even notice. They might enter our lives, catalyze an event, and leave. Or they might remain in our lives until our body dissolves. These interactions propel all to live their mandates and fulfill their intents."

"So, even the people we dislike help us create our story line. I was born the Good Little Girl who never got angry, always obeyed, and lived to please others. If I hadn't been trampled by so many players, my intent to break the martyr-victim pattern could not be actualized. And if I didn't have help from others along the way, I wouldn't have made it this far."

My Fool said, "Likewise, if my intent is to stop being a General of power, then those I interact with will be players (victims, villains, and saviors) to help me actualize my story, and I—theirs. However, players can break off at any time and end their part in the story, and be replaced by another. Further, as players seemingly die, they can just as quickly cycle back in some form to carry on the story."

I found it interesting to view our journeys this way, that just because a body dissolved, it didn't mean the story was over. Everyone is just as they should be, need to be, and indeed want to be.

I said, "So, those who upset me are just living their mandate, fueled by their references, to fulfill an intent?"

"Yes," He said, "However, that doesn't mean that you have to participate in their 'setup.' You can still make loving decisions on behalf of yourself, and stay true to *your* intent. If a wife abuses a husband, said husband can make a stand, which might result in counseling, or divorce. This happens by not judging the abuser, but by determining what is right for one's self."

I sighed. "And this brings us back to loneliness. Championing self-respect, it seems, means that one must overcome the fear of being alone."

"Yes. Braving 'the alone' is mandatory to truly learn how to be together with others. In the quiet still of 'the alone' we gaze upon the waters of our self, calm and clear. Slipping in and diving down, we touch our truest yearning, our deepest need."

I gasped in understanding. "We touch our intent."

"Yes," He affirmed. "Do not fear loneliness. It will only bring you to yourself. And when you touch yourself, you touch others. When you are with yourself, you are with others."

His words were beautiful, yet here we were in this barren, gray sand wasteland. "But we are, right now, in this desolate place and it *is* lonely. How do we get to the 'diving down' part from here? This desert looks endless."

"You can't get there from here."

Our voices blended. "The linear journey doesn't free you."

We looked at each other and laughed.

He said, "I do believe we are getting in sync. Let's walk."

"If we can't get there from here, why bother walking?"

"You were stuck in Mud Lake for so long, and you were in The Zone so briefly, activity will stimulate your blood. You see, you can take the journey, not to arrive somewhere, but rather to acquire experience and wisdom. When you are ready, and you truly embrace, 'the alone,' you will be 'diving down.' "

"So by embracing our true self, we also touch others?"

"Yes. And in that way, loneliness eases."

A body-sized rectangular mirror appeared before us. I turned my head toward Him for assurance, but He was gone. I gasped. I wasn't ready for Him to leave! I looked back to the mirror and jumped. He was *in* it!

He said from the mirror, "What you see of me is a reflection of you. I represent the wise aspect of your being. My words reflect what you already unconsciously know. You need to hear the words from the conscious world, so you attract my physical presence into your life. But try to touch me."

I reached out and touched the flat surface.

"See, you can't touch me by reaching out," He said. "The only way you have been able to find me, see me, touch me, is by going within yourself. You crossed the State Line. Go inside—deeper. Find me there."

I closed my eyes and journeyed within, searching for my Wise Self. There He was, like a constellation in the Universe. I touched Him with my mind, and felt that He was me, and I was Him. We were one and the same.

He said, "Open your eyes."

My eyes opened.

My Sweet Fool was still in the mirror talking to me. "Relating only with what we see before us prohibits genuine understanding. If you wish to touch another, then find that person in yourself."

"If you find the person within, you find the person without?"

"Yes."

A little breeze picked up, blowing my hair across my eyes. Through the tendrils, He seemed crisply real, yet so elusive—like warm sunshine sparkling on the sand, or water slipping through my hands. I brushed my hair back from my face.

"If you locate in you what you see in the outside world, such as friends and foes, family and strangers—then you will have the power to develop a new relationship with yourself. For instance: If you have a critical parent, and you look within to see your own critical self, you can work on curbing your own critical tendencies (be it self critical or otherwise). As you improve this relationship with yourself, you will respond differently to your critical parent, and that relationship will change. Conversely, the relationship you have with another, in this instance—the critical parent, can be a reflection of how you subconsciously relate with yourself."

"Oh," I said, "So, our agitation with someone else, could also reflect how we are agitated with ourselves. And if we work on that then we will not be so agitated with that person anymore."

"Yes. Your husband is a perfectionist. That stresses you. But who is the real perfectionist?"

"Me. I'm the perfectionist. So, he is a reflection of the perfectionist in me. I accept his expectations because secretly I believe I *should* be perfect. When I can't fulfill his expectations, he grows angry and points out my imperfections. I accept his ire because inwardly, I agree with him that I have failed. Yet, I blame *him* for being the perfectionist."

He added, "So, if you gave yourself permission to *not* be a perfectionist, how would you react to his prodding?"

I shrugged my shoulders. "I don't think I'd even care. I'd just go about my day happily."

"Yes. You can see why confrontation with another can be more effective if we first become aware of what is going on within, and make peace with ourselves."

"Yes," I said, "can you imagine how many arguments would not be had, if we did this? I guess people can only do to us, what we do to ourselves. Hmm. So, in summary: as we change the way we treat ourselves, it changes the way we treat others, and consequently, the way others treat us."

His brown eyes sparkled, and for a moment, the whole mirror flashed light. When I could see Him again, He said, "And also in summary: how people treat you sheds light on your own inner workings, buried emotional wounds, and the hidden self. However, if you only gaze outward, seeing people separate unto themselves, then your true self is camouflaged. Their actions might make you want to retaliate or render yourself a victim. And until you look within, these patterns will repeat."

"I feel like that is what is happening in my marriage."

"So, what aspect of yourself does your husband reflect?"

"My internal warrior."

"You chose your husband to play the part of your internal warrior, because—you won't. The price you pay for your husband's 'protection' is that you have allowed yourself to become somewhat dominated by him. And for that, you have great dislike. However, if you activated your internal warrior and protected yourself, that scenario would fade. You would stop blaming your husband for the very warrior-like nature that attracted you to him in the first place."

I paused in consternation. "But what if my inner development ends the marriage? If I change, won't our relationship change?"

"If he's ready for a new way of being with you, which is really about a new way of being with himself, you will remain together. However, if he wants to maintain the relationship as it is, it may create a separation between you. Even so, the change in you, will force him to make adjustments. Those adjustments change him. No matter what the change, the change of one affects change in many. We are all connected. We all affect each other like floating pieces that believe they are separate, but when one moves, they all move. Separation is an illusion. And the great tapestry we weave is woven by the collective. One change, changes all."

I cocked my head. "That's kind of pretty. It's like, we are all in this together. And it's empowering. Our battles with the world are really battles with ourselves. The outer world mirrors the inner world. If we make peace with ourselves, we make peace with all."

He nodded. "Sometimes that means stepping back, sitting in your center, not judging others, and not judging yourself."

I thrust my shoulders down. "I want to sit in my center."

The mirror disappeared. He stood before me.

I lowered one brow. "I know I am gazing outward, but can I touch you? I mean, I want to physically feel you this time."

"That is human, and the way it is supposed to be. Touch me, if you like."

I reached out and touched the violet sweatshirt on His arm. It felt fairly solid. I sighed with relief. "The physical you is still with me."

His eyes narrowed into an almost condescending look.

I blushed. "I understand we are all One and can never really leave each other, but I still fear being alone."

He sighed briskly, turned around, and walked back the way we had come.

I said, "You aren't leaving me, are you? I mean, can I join you?"

He spoke over His shoulder. "I can never leave you, and I am always with you. But yes, you can walk with me."

I scampered up next to Him, walking along His side. "Isn't this the direction we just came from?"

He looked at me askance with narrowed eyes, as if I should know better than to say such a thing.

I swallowed, "Well, it's just that I'd like to tread new ground, even if we aren't really going anywhere."

"Like most humans, and even animals," He said, "you are curious." He cracked a faint smile and turned sideways. He extended an arm in a new direction. "This way?"

I smiled with a nod. I liked being heard. Maybe I was listening to myself. On we walked in our new unimportant direction. "From what you have told me, curiosity is a good thing."

"Curiosity makes the world go around."

I watched my boots stepping one foot in front of the other. I glanced back to view our prints, proof of our existence. Yet, my existence was still so shrouded. I exhaled in dismay and focused on the barren emptiness ahead. The Desert of Loneliness was so boring, no shrubs, bugs, or anything. I was grateful He was here to stimulate my mind.

I bumped into something in front of me. I gasped, "Oh!" and stepped back holding my hand over my mouth in surprise. It was My Nun, swaddled in a black habit, desperate eyes peering from what little of her face showed.

I cried, "What are you doing here!"

She dropped to her knees, hands clasped together in prayer. "Don't murder me!"

My Fool walked on, as if this had not occurred.

"Hey," I shouted to His back. "I've got a problem here."

He answered over His shoulder, "Don't acknowledge her. Walk through what you think is there."

I examined My Nun's seemingly three-dimensional form. Walk through her? Even if I could manage to walk through her, I pitied her, and would feel bad leaving her by the wayside.

My Fool's footsteps sounded fainter. I looked to Him. He was far ahead of me for only seconds to have passed—a little like time-lapse photography. His body was growing smaller against the gloomy gray horizon. I feared He'd disappear from view. I told myself, *The Nun's an illusion, something I created.* I stepped forward, and walked clean through her as if she was not there. I did it! It worked!

My Nun shrieked.

I walked on, mumbling, "I'm sorry, I'm sorry."

I ran hard until I caught up to My Fool, breathless.

He talked as if I'd never left His side. "Shift from viewing your facades, to viewing your authentic self. Instead of cleaning the house because you want to be deemed a good housekeeper, clean it because you want it clean, or don't clean it if you don't care."

"It is so hard to do that though."

"Yes, facades have long been our shield. They protect us, yet cage us in a static repeat of events: like the woman who marries three alcoholic husbands, or the man who continues losing jobs. Facades prevent us from changing ourselves. When we wear them, our intrinsic significance cannot be seen, and deep down inside, we are lonely. The beginning is now. Reality is now, freshly created. Embracing your core self creates life change. Trust the changes."

He pointed ahead.

I saw a silvery city and started to get excited, hoping for a hot shower and a soft bed. Then the city changed to a gray ocean. The ocean changed to a huge underground cavern. The cavern changed to a night sky.

He said, "Image is like a mirage. When you try to dissolve it, it takes new shape, still covering up the inner substance. The image looks real, but when you reach it, nothing is there: like goals that promise happiness, like facades that promise significance."

"You know," I said, "one could get depressed realizing that everything we've been told about life—isn't."

"Come home to yourself, "He said, "and even facades will be cherished. They play their part to help you play yours."

I answered, "But, I *really* don't want them to guide me anymore. Not letting them lead—is hard."

"Facades have been long in the making. Shifting to a broader way of being requires time and a measure of astuteness."

I glanced about me, and did a double take. The Nun had been

trailing behind. An almost evil glint shot from her eyes and cut into me like razorblades. She mouthed, "I want you."

I realized then how lonely I'd been cloaked in my facades. I never wanted to be a backseat driver to them—ever again! They never listened anyway. With my mind, I yanked from My Nun the part of me she already had. My body jolted so hard I almost fell.

"See," He said, "You can surpass her. She is not bad, but how you use her will make a difference. There might be a time when you need to be resolute. Your nun nature can help. If you feel stuck in stubbornness, it is time to loosen her hold on you."

I glanced over my shoulder. She seemed gone . . . for now. I sighed. "Why can't she understand what we are trying to do? Can't she understand how *right* this is?"

"A facade will tell *you* what is right and wrong. It will tell you *who* is right and wrong. It will chastise you and confuse you and make you feel like nothing is real or worthwhile without it. It is the way facades were constructed. It the way it is supposed to be!"

"But My Nun is wrong. All facades are wrong because they operate from a single point of view without seeing the whole picture."

"They are not wrong, just masks that give character to stories. It's our choice whether we wear them or not. And there is nothing wrong with wearing them. Wearing them brings a certain kind of experience. If you no longer desire that experience, you can quit wearing them. There are no mistakes. Our thoughts accumulate and eventually create a direction that we play out, and keep playing until the story is finished. Consequences follow every action. No one gets away with anything, nor is anyone truly cheated. Life brings all to balance no matter what anyone does. However, the way you experience life will differ depending on your relationship between your facades and yourself."

"Okay, I get it. I will stop judging them. I just want to be free. I crave my authentic self expression."

"Craving leads to action. What would it be like to experience this or that? Outsiders may scold and say, don't tempt fate. Don't step outside convention. But often, remaining bound feels analogous to a bud being told it can't flower, or a sky being told it can't rain."

My hand went to my heart. "I can relate to that. Who doesn't grow weary of running around in circles like a hamster on a wheel? The housewife serving her family twenty-four hours a day, the father working himself into the grave, the soul-sucking dead-end job, the perpetual victim too numb to cry anymore, the never ending clamor of a yelping parent, the constant berating of an abusive mate—all life long. The martyr gives, gives, and gives . . . all life long. The avenger takes, takes, and takes . . . all life long. Sooner or later, change is craved. Some sort of change, sometimes, any kind of change!"

"Well said, Susan!" His head bobbed approvingly, "your wisdom is flourishing."

"So," I continued, in conclusion, "Curiosity sparks adventure, and our issues motivate solutions. Forging new paths in our own unique way, we seek our own brand of fulfillment, granting ourselves freedom from the little hamster wheels of repeat all sitting in a row. Little Red Riding Hood *can* leave the village! The big bad wolf is the shadow lurking in the unknown, deterring most to a life of wheel running encouraged by social groups. In this, the group is secured with shared belief that their way is the right way."

"Careful." He smiled. "Preaching freedom from the 'wheel' will likely insult those content in their pattern. To them, their wheel is the best, shiniest, most valuable wheel in the world. They may hiss and spit at you and tell you that you are wrong, and that it is you who are lost and you who are doomed. If their mandate is to see what it is like to round a particular wheel, nothing anyone can say or do will change that. They will be offended, and they will deem you offensive."

I opened my mouth to rebut, trying to see a way around His forecast, a way to free the people from the wheel. But then I realized that my savior facade had risen, proclaiming wheel running bad—when in fact, until every wheel is run, the craving for wheel running won't end. So my mouth just hung there open in the air. Who was I to talk? I'd been wheel running all my life.

"Yes, Susan," He smiled warmly, "that is right. There is nothing wrong with wheel running, and you need not save everyone, or anyone. And what is more—you can't. You can only save yourself. And when the others are ready, they will do the same. Every person is imbued with a sense of life direction. They don't require your guidance, even though guiding them or helping them might be an agreed upon scene in your mutual story. All stories have value, each and every one."

"But it is hard to let people be ignorant."

"We are all ignorant," He said. "If you want to be free of your own wheel, focus on your own ignorance."

I felt humbled, and I had to keep The Nun from rising in me.

He added, "*We* put the judgmental spin on our life events, 'I matter because someone wants to marry me.' 'I don't matter because I never graduated High School.' It is up to the individual, if it is within their intent, to cease judgment, and adhere to the intrinsic significance of every being."

I quite suddenly felt my significance. Tears glossed my eyes. I could write, take care of my children, and curl my hair, without commanding myself at *all costs to my sanity* to be a *perfect* writer, *perfect* mother, or *perfect* in appearance. I could behave in manners that felt healthy to me. I blurted, "My behavior is *my* choice."

"Yes. Only your facade bade you sacrifice yourself. When you wear your facade, you cannot help but react in accordance to it—be it 'poor me', 'ain't I the cat's meow', or 'smarty pants.' "

I said, "Interesting how facades basically run our world." I stared at my boots walking, noticing they were smothered in dust. Dust covers the shoes, but we usually don't notice until it is too late. Only when our shoes are buried in dust do we realize that what is beneath the dust can't be seen. Only then do we realize we are lost.

A gale of wind kicked up and blew tendrils of My Fool's hair back. Three tendrils stuck up on His head and glistened in a salmon-colored light. He stopped walking. His lids, shiny with sweat, slipped over His eyes. He inhaled slowly yet mightily, sucking in the wind. The corner of His eye glimmered, and became a tear growing fatter. But before it fell, He threw His hands up, freeing words charged with power, yet gently spoken. "This day of days . . . I walk the winds. I behold . . . true self."

My heart ached for a moment, and then swelled into something big. The wind breathed into my ears, sweeping through the vast caverns of my inner world. My spine felt stretched down to the earth's core and up to the heavens.

The gale passed. His eyes opened. He sighed and thrust His chest out, chin up, and swallowed. Then He half-laughed in pain. "Vulnerability was never my strong suit." He gave me a sidelong glance, "removing armor—hurts."

I stood in soothing silence, being . . . real. But there was a loneliness to it. What was loneliness? Then I knew. "It is lonely, being *real* that is . . . in a world that isn't."

He smiled faintly. "This *is* the Desert of Loneliness."

"How is it that you, a man of wisdom, visit here so often?"

His eyes shimmered in a sea of something painfully beautiful, yet unfulfilled. He spoke in a low tone that bespoke an artist constrained from putting the final stroke on his masterpiece. "I have memories of being a conductor who composed music that vibrated to the energy of all things before they 'become.' This experience produced the most exquisite joy, and . . . the most excruciating pain. My music swept over the public, disturbing their comfort region, their hamster wheel, so to speak. They had an opportunity to heighten their consciousness, to get off the wheel, but they rejected deeper awareness. This rejection wounded me. Playing such music now, is bittersweet. When the music flows, I swell with elation. Yet beneath that swell is an unquenchable ache, not only from retained memories, but because I myself cannot quite become what I'm hearing. Even the music does not fully capture the *purest* Creative Energy."

My chest felt heavy with His sadness.

He said, "I have been many things: a warrior with horse and sword, an official in the halls of government, a laborer in the fields of love. But nothing compares to composing music, expressing life's vibrations beyond words. Though anguish goes with it, composing music, for me, is a form unrivaled for channeling Creative Energy unimpeded by conscious thought. I long for that."

"You are heading that way though, I mean Highway Eleven," I bowed my head forlornly, "or so you have said."

"Yes. I call it forth to loosen the cement that locks me in this story called earth. Just a few loose ends need tending. This day of days, I'm tangled in the sticky web of illusion that I cannot touch the purest form of Creative Energy. I can see it, taste it, smell it, but touch it . . . I cannot."

I sighed on quivering breath, feeling His pain.

He stood there, long face revealing ancient sadness. His words dripped thick and slow, "Loneliness presses me to the edge. Failure to touch the beauty I sense causes more pain than this self can bear."

I rested an affectionate hand on His shoulder.

He jolted.

I withdrew.

"Sorry," He said, "habit."

"That's okay. I feel your frustration."

His body trembled. His melancholy voice seemed to wail and whisper to every inch of this never-ending desert, called Loneliness. "I have one foot planted in the perceived world, and the other foot floating in uncharted energy searching for Highway Eleven. I truly am a 'half man.' Today the human half has me."

He wouldn't let me touch Him, so I smiled gently. "It's difficult to place your foot where people can't see."

"Yes. The inability to place it makes centering difficult. A one-legged man loses balance, yet planting the other foot on a moving fluid target viewed through the screen door of my perception, is challenge worth any contest."

"Why can't you push down the screen door and jump into the fluid world with both feet?"

"My lingering desire to orchestrate binds me to the mundane world. I love to orchestrate, but now I must surrender, not control. The desire to control keeps the screen door intact, and hardens the glue that keeps me here. This day, the mountain does not vanish. My magic is poor. So many highways, byways, and avenues beg to be chased, a chase that could go on beyond the end of seeming time. But I will not be diverted. I have one last wound to address."

His arms rose to the sky, summoning, "Come symphony!" His voice cracked, and everything within Him became everything shouting from Him, "Break the web. Cut me loose from the past. Cut me loose from the future. Let me become the moment! The moment. The moment. The moment. The moment. The moment. The moment." He was there, totally there, all gathered, all together, condensed into a laser beam projecting outward. "The moment, the moment, the moment." Lightning bolts shot into His fingers. His body convulsed lightly. "The moment, the moment, the moment." Then He was still. He whispered, 'The moment, the moment, the moment." He lowered His arms and bowed His head, saying softly, "It is done."

I blinked back a tear. "Are you all right?"

He raised His head slowly, liquid eyes carrying something I'd never before seen and to this day I do not know what it was. His body was less dense and His voice sounded like a dream. "As I release my hold on the world, it reflects a new reflection. This moment, I have released expectations. Each identity will find its own journey, and discover, release, and dissolve all experience, without me to guide them. I will not project my views, decide what's right or wrong, or endeavor to pave the way for others. I free myself from this heavy obligation. Freedom is the brightest light. Freedom is fluid. Perception is binding. Soon, I will be bound no more, for I am the 'we.' And the 'we' is the Creator and the Creation."

His eyes looked like tunnels. I wanted to travel inside them. I started too, but suddenly, I was distracted. A sign appeared, hanging on the tip of His nose. I almost laughed, but I didn't want to appear disrespectful. Swallowing humor, I asked, "What's the sign for? Why is it hanging on your nose?"

"To remind me of my true intent to flow Pure Creative Energy beyond all perception and conclude my earth story."

I felt tearful. I didn't want My Fool to leave me. "I want to conclude my earth story too."

He looked into me knowingly. The nose sign dissolved. "You have much left to explore on this earth: the many untouched corners of beauty, closets of mystery, and oceanic power. You have yet to experience many wonderful earth forms, thoughts, and emotions—for you have been busy hiding under covers. Explore mind, heart, body, and spirit. Behold earth, air, water, and fire. Travel north, east, south, and west. Learn about past and future, male and female, positive and negative, cycles and stagnation."

He was making earth life sound so good. I usually focused on the world's pain.

"Celebrate life, Susan. Live with gusto!"

I sighed, "It's just so scary!"

"Live the mystery."

The mystery, I thought, is what makes life exciting. Exploring the mystery was as taking ourselves back slowly bit by bit, and yet becoming more than we were by having taken the journey. "The journey changes us, doesn't it?"

His eyes glimmered. "The journey alone brightens our being and changes the Universe. We finish the earth journey in a way, by growing into it, like a crab that grows into its shell, and then one day outgrows it and leaves. In that same way, we can experiment with energy, manifest ideas, brighten curiosity, and come face to face with 'what if.' When we free flow the experience of 'what if,' we ride the river with open eyes, and shake off the conscious mind. Then wisdom rises from the deepest, purest part of us through impulses. Not the impulses that come from our facades, like, 'I want to deck that guy for giving me a dirty look,' or 'I want to hide in my room because my mommy yelled at me.' Wisdom comes from the deep within where dwells the inner sage that knows intrinsic significance of all. In tapping that vibration, words arise like, 'I am worthy, so I will speak up for myself,' or 'I am worthy, so I don't need to react to that insult.' Following these sagacious wisdoms that rise from one's self requires courage. The true leap of faith is to trust life—not a person, or doctrine, or a 'way.' But Life itself."

I nodded. "Trust life, "I murmured, "just trust life."

"Following this flow is as riding the stream to the sea, deflecting public opinion, and being an original." He stepped back from me as if preparing to leave. He gazed upon me almost paternally. "May your image become unnecessary. May your facades weaken. May you discover wisdom and joy, time and timelessness . . . through yourself. Who are you? You're nobody, and everybody." He took another step back. "Ain't—Life—Great!"

Suddenly I felt bone weary. All that work breaking free from Mud Lake had done me in.

"Rest," He said, "regenerate."

"If I sleep, will you be gone when I awaken?"

He nodded.

"Where are you going?"

"I will leave the Desert and go into the Quicksand."

"The Quicksand?"

"The Quicksand leads to the Cave of Wounds. I have work to do."

"You can leave the Desert of Loneliness that easily?"

"I've learned." He smiled faintly. "You will too."

I looked at My Fool skeptically, still not quite trusting my ability to attain what I so badly wanted—wisdom and courage.

"Open your pack," He said.

I opened it, knowing He would give me another gem. I was excited to see what color it would be. He dropped an opaque blue-gray stone in my pack. It landed on my white silk scarf. What appeared opaque in the gem soon cleared. The blue-gray that at first seemed rustic and ugly had become see-through crystalline beauty with light blue hints in the shine of it. Then it turned bright crystal clear blue, reminding me of clear sky. He said, "This is the Gem of Independence, first experienced as loneliness. Beyond loneliness lies your essence. Beyond your essence is all essence . . . Pure Creative Energy. Loneliness fades. Freedom is found and the boundless open sky is there to explore."

"Thank you," I said, closing my pack. "I will change the gray of loneliness to the beauty of independence and freedom by seeking quintessence."

"Remember, it lies in no direction. It's found by believing in yourself and in life by following your own way and singing your own song, despite the reaction of others."

"I'll remember."

"You probably won't."

I furrowed my brows. "I won't?"

"When we panic, our wisdom fades into the flurry of out-of-kilter emotions and thoughts."

"Are you saying I'll panic soon?"

"Susan, you are almost always in a constant state of panic."

I almost laughed, because He was right, but I wanted to cry because He wasn't wrong.

"Learning to be calm will still the waters and let your wisdom rise again. When you are panicked, reflect on that."

I nodded and sank to the ground, too weary to stand any longer. I rested my back on the soft sand, warm and comforting against my damp, dirty body.

His words washed over me like a melody resounding in my brain, as if the Him in me were speaking. "You are lovable as you are. Be kind to yourself. You are an original standing alone, yet a collective that is everyone. Everyone is okay, including you. No one need change, but if you seek modification, require it from no other. If you change, those around you will change, as they are reflections of yourself. One person transforming, changes the world, even if only a sliver."

With those words, I sank into a subterranean sleep.

When I awoke, He was gone. And I felt, well . . . lonely.

I knew the linear walk would not terminate my loneliness, so I didn't bother traveling far. I knew no knight in shining armor would rescue me, so I didn't bother hoping for one. Days and days passed. I couldn't shake the loneliness. I kept hoping that soon I'd see beauty, like the murky blue-gray gem that suddenly appeared a clear beautiful blue. I kept hoping that the price for independence would be paid, and freedom attained. I hadn't seen Him in weeks. Somehow, I knew He was on His own adventure, overcoming some hurdle I hadn't discovered yet.

I spent my days in gentle meditations, attempting to be content being with myself. I wanted someone to acknowledge me. I wanted someone to agree with me. I wanted someone to love me. However, even *if* someone actually did those things, why should I believe *their* perception? What did anyone truly know of me? Certainly not as much as I knew of me. So what worth was their judgment, be it good or bad?

No. I was on my own, even if another did acknowledge me. Still, I didn't like being misunderstood. My husband deemed me weird. My peers nodded politely, not really understanding me at all. And strangers, well, I dared not reveal myself to strangers. If my loved ones didn't understand me, how could they?

My loneliness grew and grew and grew, mounting into a ferocious windstorm that whipped sand crystals into my eyes, teeth, and hair, and grated painfully against my skin. I huddled in a ball on hands and knees, feeling my hair frenzy into tangled knots.

I cried to the Universe, "See me, hear me, know me!" I wanted to be real in this world, but it seemed no one could touch the true me. I felt *unreal.* I felt like a speck of dust, inconsequential to the whole of life. I'd left the herd of society where conformity bought company, and institutions offered safety. I had strayed to find my independence. And this was the price I paid. I was in a black, dark, and lonely place. This independence, this independence—oh the price was high! Gaining independence required treading no known path. Trekking the unknown. That was the risk. 'Live the mystery,' My Fool had said, but I was afraid.

I covered my ears to block the howling sound, but I couldn't block the beating gush of wind upon my body. I was so exposed. Nowhere to run. Nowhere to hide. No shelter for me now. The Old World was not an option. The New World seemed out of reach. I started to cry, feeling abandoned, even by myself. Where was my divinity? Where was my sage in the great within? I was so lonely.

I saw Him then, oh not Him, but the Him in me—my sagacious aspect. My forehead felt like it was opening. I was doing more than touching the Him in me. I was touching Him through me. More and more, it seemed there was no difference between the me in Him, or the Him *in* me, or Him *and* me. Anyway, I knew that at this very moment, He was suffering . . . privately. Even though He'd erected a wall between us to shelter His vulnerability, I could feel His pain. For His pain was mine.

I looked at Him inside me, at Him wherever He was.

The wind wailed louder, screaming the agony that could not come from His lips.

I had reached Him. His words echoed in my brain. "I am in the Cave of Wounds accessing retained emotions of my Core Wound. No matter how often I dissolve the screen door that filters Pure Creative Energy, the Core Wound recreates it. The purest notes and melodies are bunched against the screen holes, unable to reach me. Healing this wound will dissolve the screen door permanently."

His words mounted in me, for I felt it too, the wild kicking and screaming of a pure me trying to break free of the perceived self! Oh, what torment, to hear the great heartbeat of creation's genesis, but to be blocked from bringing it through consciousness in its pure form! The artist who sees the picture she cannot bring to canvas. The writer who feels the essence he cannot put into words. The child who feels the moon, and blows it a kiss goodnight, because she doesn't know how else to express herself. It isn't enough. Could anything ever be? Can ecstasy be conveyed? Can pure wisdom be channeled? Can Creative Energy in its pure state converge with three-dimensional beings? I had to believe it. I had to believe that we could experience this caliber of connection, significance, and belonging. Isn't that what all humans search for?

People call it love, but even that word falls short. The most misunderstood word in the human experience . . . is love. In the multiple definitions of love, the greatest love has no definition. It surpasses human comprehension, for it bears no conditions or separations. What human can fathom that kind of love, each and every moment of his or her life?

"Walk the winds!" His words cried out in my mind.

Like magic, Jean Sibelius *Violin Concerto #1* played across the desert, soaking into me. I let the symphony take me, for I could no longer contain the loneliness. I rose in the howling wind. Grit stung my face. I pushed against the force with a resounding determination that left no room for surrender. I would become the symphony. I would! I wanted this more than anything, ever, in my whole life.

Long tears streaked my dusty face, blowing excess liquid behind me into the winds of oblivion. The symphony became an axe that shattered the walls that had kept me lonely. The winds crashed into each other as if arguing about which way to blow. My hair whipped my face in a tangled mass. Through thick flying sand, and the strands of my frenzied hair, I saw a forked road. One path yielded to the ordinary past, a life of static repeat that ensures a known future. The other path, obscure and unfamiliar, yielded to the ever-changing extraordinary present. I was at choice point.

Even no choice was a choice. I did not hesitate. I wanted the path of the ever-changing extraordinary present. Somehow, I knew it would give me what I sought when first I crossed the State Line.

"Then do that," He whispered with an eerie warmth.

He and I cried out, two voices as one, "Freedom!"

I tried to step onto the path, but an air current pushed up my foot and almost made me fall backwards. I tried again, and again. I couldn't take the step no matter how badly I wanted . . . needed to move forward. I finally fell in a heap staring longingly through slapping wind at the path I wanted to tread. A barrage of feelings flooded me, and I could express none of them.

I felt helpless. These perceptions had such a hold on me. Perceptions are more than viewing machines; they are identities. My perception of My Nun *is* My Nun, and no matter how many times I break free, she seems to have a hold on me.

Our facades' stubborn insistence on upholding image was *beyond words*. The fear of releasing perception and changing was *beyond words*. The urgency to expand awareness and the behold Pure Creative Energy was *beyond words*! Beyond words is what words cannot hold. Yes, that was my destination—beyond words.

I pushed myself forward on hands and knees, stretching my fingers toward the chosen path. I also had an aerial view of myself trying to crawl on the ground. I felt real watching myself, and the self on hands and knees seemed like an image in the mirror. It is not enough to recognize image, fight it, or refuse to feed it. For still, when you look in the mirror, the image is there, begging you to take hold again. Can I look into the mirror and see beyond my image? Can I?

I coughed, spitting out a hunk of sand that almost flew down my windpipe. Doubt choked me. I stopped trying to move forward for a moment, laboring to breathe.

Tones of the symphony played over me like bow to violin. The notes seem to say, *Challenge the doubt. When gaining ground in dissolving image, the image resorts to its last defense—doubt. Doubt cripples and impedes, so challenge it. Sever it quickly. Break facade, image, and perceptions of limitation.*

Even as I caught my breath, my lungs screamed pain. My ears

screamed pain. I screamed pain. All my various facades shot up from the ground before me like the dead rising from graves in a horror movie. They wailed, pleading, "Have mercy, don't eradicate us! You must keep us as we are! You need us to cloak you from the hardships of life!"

I thought I shouted back, but I was screaming, "I am more than facade! I . . . am . . . more!" I screamed repeatedly in a trance-like state, "I am more!" And there was a magic in it. With all that I was, I pushed myself forward on hands and knees inching, inching through the graveyard of my selves along my chosen path. Determination drenched my cheeks with burning tears, and my words scorched command. "All masks dissolve into one . . . pure . . . self."

Then suddenly, I remembered My Fool's dissertation on panic. I calmed down and focused on my quintessence. And I remembered how He'd taught me that shifting focus was the magic carpet from one place to another.

I envisioned myself moving toward my quintessence, nothing more. And then I crawled faster, easier, farther.

I crawled past my facades unsure how they'd respond. What would I become without my facades to identify me? Did it matter? For I knew what I had been when under their rule, and certainly what I'd again be if I surrendered. I'd be right back in Mud Lake.

I saw myself as a star shining bright. I was the star, here, now. I crawled over a man's tracks, cemented into the land of loneliness. They were My Fool's tracks. I knew it, I felt Him bubble up into my heart as I crossed over them. I'd covered this ground before and never saw tracks, but then old ground is new ground when you walk it in new ways. His loneliness had broken Him. And now it was breaking me. Or maybe it was not us it was breaking, but our perceptions of mundane reality. Maybe that felt like death, to be that one grain of salt that did not go through the hourglass, but instead blew free outside the confines of time. How could freedom be lonely? Maybe it wasn't. Maybe I just viewed it that way.

Then, as quick as breath, I didn't fear what others might feel toward me. Nor did I fear losing conscious memory of who I'd believed myself to be. Even if I grew two heads, turned green, went blind, or became poor—fear . . . did not have me. Pure Creative

Energy did. If I succeeded in releasing the small self to the large self, new awareness *would* create new form, and a new way of being. That could be expected, for the new cannot arrive when focused on the old. The old must be lost for the new to be found. I only felt lonely because I was staring at the hourglass filled with those I knew. But when I turned away, the sky was filled with all kinds of life. I wasn't really alone!

I crawled forward onto the ever-changing path of the present, chanting, "Pure Creative Energy flows through me. I am a star. I am a star. A star. A star." I wanted to chant, "I am everything," but everything seemed too challenging to conceptualize at the moment. I needed a clear and potent focus to distract me from my howling facades who yet followed me, crawling, begging for attention. In the past, when I gave them attention, I experienced their perceptions and lived according to their views. Their views filtered Creative Energy from manifesting purely. The clouds of perception dim the bright and clear picture that become screens between Creator and Creation: impeding the painter from painting the unpaintable thing, the composer from composing something just beyond his reach, the consciousness from actualizing untapped resources, such as extra sensory perception, and illumination.

What drove Van Gogh insane? Why was he so frustrated with his art, when today it sells for millions? Where does the term an artist's temperament come from? Musicians, writers, artists, and others in creative fields, have long suffered torment from touching absolute purity in realms unknown, but unable to pull that purity from the cosmos into the three-dimensional world.

If the artist can't release her intellectual conclusion of herself and the world, then she creates only a small part of what she truly intended to flow. If I am to flow purely, I must not be cemented by my howling selves. I must loosen the current perceptions that hold my form together. I invite quantum change by releasing direction.

Conviction came. I released everything. Everything. I focused only on Pure Creative Energy flowing through me, unimpeded. I inhaled deeply and rose to my feet, arms spreading open to Creation. What ever happens—happens! I headed into the wind without a rudder. With my next step, I fell into a void, like quicksand, falling. Falling into nowhere, everywhere, anywhere.

The symphony ended. I, as I knew myself to be—ended.

Can you free the part of you that is bound in self-perception? The you that drinks other people's reactions, and belches or coos depending on the flavor. The you that ever judges yourself guilty, innocent, or on probation, deserving a beer, or a hit in the head. The you who pretends that secret emptiness isn't there, and that a life of rote is not . . . so . . . bad.

Do you have a song to sing, but *today is not the time or place*? Do you want to scream, "I matter!" but *today is not the time or place*? Do you want to rest and replenish, but *today is not the time or place*? Do you ever wonder if the time and place will *ever* come when you can feel the sun on your skin, your heart flower, or your mind open Universe wide?

Can you let the part of you end that worries and wonders if you did right or if someone else did wrong. If you will be loved when you're old, or crave the zeal of youth. If bad fortune will befall you, or good luck uplift you. Or if you'll live long, or die young?

Can you let the part of you end that fears cancer, AIDS, depression, panic attacks, economical collapse, or the destruction of the world? The you that worries if you'll get that raise, retire, become lazy, get Medicare, or care. The you that worries you might live and die and forget life happened, or that death might turn you to dust, or send you to hell?

Do you know? Do you really know any answers at all? How do you know? What makes you know? How can you be certain? Is your faith blind? Are you blind? Are you in a coffin you call life, or have you just learned to accept the restriction?

All right, all right, only the truly courageous will continue beyond this page. And each time you read this book your journey will be anew, and your experience a level deeper. Assess your desire this day of days, and this night of nights. If you want to feel the cells in your body shine like a million suns, then forge this desert, my friends. Brave the winds. I'll meet you soon with stars in my hands.

Cave of Wounds
"If you don't own the wound, the wound will own you."

GEM #6 STRIFE

Down I fell, away from the Desert of Loneliness into thick quicksand that slowed me, but did not stop me from sliding through. Down, down, down. The journey seemed unending. But it did end. Eventually the sand gave way to air, and I fell hard, smacking my knees on solid dark ground. Shrill pains shot up my thighs. I was in a deep hole. Light crept through slits in a ceiling a few hundred feet above.

I gulped. Where was I now? What had my persistence earned me? I looked around. I was in a cave. Purple black walls dripped water. Tunnels spiraled everywhere. Faint tones of classical music sounded from the largest tunnel. Was He in here?

I rose stiffly. Blood dripped down my knees, warm and sticky, soaking around the edges of my torn jeans, ripped to my thighs by the fall. Maybe I was trying a little too hard to get to my core. Day by day, my clothes wore thinner. Soon I would be naked.

I limped toward the music into the largest tunnel along side an underground stream. Deep black waters glimmered from light that found entrance from tiny openings in the cavern ceiling. My path slanted downward, a bit moist and slippery, deeper, and darker until I was blind. I edged my way carefully around a corner to the chamber where Richard Strauss's, *Death and Transfiguration* played, bouncing off the walls in chilling beauty.

Burning purple candles lined rock wall edges, secreting a lavender scent. I didn't see Him at first, but then I noticed a shadowy figure sitting on a bulge of cave rock. My eyes adjusted to the dark. The figure took on definition. I stared at its back. A purple-black robe cloaked the figure. The movement of an arm indicated that the figure was writing.

"Welcome to the Cave of Wounds," He said, without turning to see me.

It was My Fool, of course. I replied, "I felt your pain from the Desert of Loneliness. I'm glad I found you."

His voice reverberated, enveloping the room like a god. But His tone was somber, empty of something He couldn't attain. He stopped writing. "I frequent this cave, though my journey be one way. Each time I come here, I am a changed person. Thus the cave seems changed. My experience is new. I can play the same symphony a hundred times, each time hearing it differently, each time using its vibration as an agent for change."

He pointed to a massive spider web spread before Him, spanning from ceiling to floor, and just as wide. Candlelight made the silken mesh almost moon-like. He said, "I have observed this web from its beginnings, a single strand growing into a gossamer masterpiece born from—strife."

I walked toward Him.

He commanded, "Stop."

I froze, still about ten feet away.

His voice was stern. "I will face you soon, but not quite yet. However, I will share my insights if you care to hear."

"I care to hear." I stood frozen.

He sighed on quivering breath, as if gathering pain from anguished places to lend power to His statement. Though His voice was aimed at the web, the cave echoed it throughout the room, quite clearly. "Those who enter the Cave of Wounds are ready to understand the wisdom of strife: how it is perpetuated, the magic it creates, and how it is resolved."

I said softly, "I *would* like to understand those things."

"Subjective perceptions lead us to conclude skewed beliefs about the right and wrong of people, events, and ourselves. This frequently causes strife. We might cast blame on ourselves, 'I'm no good because I was abandoned.' 'I always mess up because I'm stupid.' Or, we might vilify others. 'His criticism destroyed my self-esteem.' 'She wrecked my life with her selfish ways.' These beliefs create motion. Events are catalyzed. These events turn into marvelous yarns and adventurous stories. However, the greatest part of any story is the ending, where insight and meaning are embraced. This happens when we finally understand our pain, where it really came from, what it really is, and why we have felt it."

My knees stung, but I stayed still and focused. "So understanding our pain, enables us to release it, so a story can end?"

He rose and faced me at last, while yet keeping his distance. Candlelight shone in His glossy eyes flashing like a cat in the night. "Yes. There can be many stories in one lifetime. Each story represents a pattern or way of being. Each story is perpetuated by a Core Wound, such as severe neglect, the victim of torture, or perhaps an accident. If you choose to end one story and begin another, then the original wound must at last, heal. You can spend your whole life hating those who wronged you—your cruel father, your alcoholic mother, your insensitive boss—and the story cannot end, even if your life does. It will just carry on in some other reality, for your story, designed by you as Creative Energy, exists for a great reason. Fulfillment will be had, and benefits reaped—eventually."

I said, with aching legs, "It's like, there are gifts in every story, and our strife is the catalyst to find those gifts." I glanced at the massive spider web.

"Yes," He said. "The spider web is all we have woven from the first stone thrown. The first stone thrown is a Core Event that created a Core Wound. The effects of this wound ripple outward creating a massive story that continues even now. The Core Wound is covered so thickly, we often don't know it is there. It may have even originated before one's current self came into being. Sometimes we have flashes or feelings that make no sense to our current identity. For instance, you Susan, who have no religious background, are deeply connected to the vibration of a cloistered nun. The nun story began before you were born."

I nodded. "That makes so much sense."

He said, "These long-forgotten first events are the springboard for strings of thoughts, that formed beliefs, that led to actions, that created patterns (sometimes spanning lifetimes), that make us who we are today."

"So, what we feel and how we came to be as we are—is seldom comprehended."

"No, it isn't," He said, "Until the Core Wound is healed, it is ever fresh and easily aggravated, spilling over into our current life in bizarre, maybe even inappropriate ways that seem to defy conscious understanding. The woman who won't let blonde-haired men touch her. (Maybe in another life experience, she was murdered by a blonde-haired man.) The man who bottles his feelings. (Maybe as a toddler, he saw his mother beaten for expressing hers.) Our behaviors might seem illogical or wrong, but the feelings behind them are valid. If we could but see that these behaviors are natural reactions to a hidden wound, then our ignorant judging would cease. By addressing the Core Wound that began the story, we can change unwanted behavior. However, since we do not generally do this, we usually deem our bruised or combative feelings a result of something recent, and often someone else's fault."

"Wow," I said. "So, healing Core Wounds can help us change life long patterns."

"Yes." He rose and walked up to me. He gestured for me to sit. "You look uncomfortable standing."

I drew myself down to the cool smooth ground, sitting in a half-lotus. I did feel better.

He sat directly in front of me, appearing a shadow away from the candlelight. "Our dissociation with the Core Wound results in much self-imposed anguish and unpleasant behavior. Misconceptions abound."

I thought of my nun-like nature that promoted the dark belief that suffering made me worthy. What happened to make me that way? What Core Wound was responsible for that? Then I thought about my work. I said, "I have seen how misconceptions operate when I do couples counseling. Each person jumps to erroneous beliefs about the other, based on their own insecurities, both out of touch with the truth. Once the session is over and the truth is out, suffering diminishes."

"That is an example of healing surface wounds."

"Surface wounds?"

"Locating, owning, and healing any psychological wound is helpful, but ending a theme, or the larger story requires addressing the Core Wound. If not, even a mere insult can trigger the Core Wound locked away in the underworld of our being, and cause unpleasant reactions."

I cocked my head. "You mean, like the father who emotionally combusts on his family if a toy is on the floor, because as a child he was beaten if he made messes?"

He said, "It can go back even farther."

I added, "Like before that, perhaps in another embodiment, he was poor, never had a toy, and therefore deems his child unappreciative. Then going back and back to the Core Wound?"

"Yes," He said. "A Core Wound holds a story. Each story sprung from a Core Wound. In the course of our earth journey, linearly speaking, we each incurred a series of Core Wounds that launched a series of stories. But what story are we currently living that perhaps we are ready to end? And if we are not ready, then retained emotion from the past will continually emerge in the present."

I said, "I once knew a man who walked about whistling, never facing pressing emotional issues, pretending all was fine. Yet, little things angered him. His whistle interchanged a dozen times a day, with a red face and popping veins because the butter is in the wrong place in the refrigerator, there is a sticky spot on the floor, or there is a fly in the house. Beneath his rosy perceptions of his life, anger held permanent residence inside him because he never explored its roots."

He said, "And that is the man's right, for he too has a story to be had, and a necessary nature, with necessary perceptions, to live a mandate, to fulfill his intent. Those around him will respond in ways to likewise live their mandate and fulfill their intent."

My mind flashed on the *Star Trek Enterprise* sailing through outer space. "So, we all control our own ship. If we feel controlled, it is because we have abdicated control."

His shadowy head nodded. "If you understand this, blame ceases. If you choose to change your destination, take charge of the helm, change *your* coordinates, and stop trying to change the coordinates of others."

His ghost-like figure emitted a soft energy that soaked into my body. I became deeply calmed and my knees didn't hurt anymore. I said, "It's difficult to let people be themselves, and to stop trying to turn them into what we want them to be."

"Yes, but their Core Wound is *their* business. Core Wounds exist for a reason. Once the reason has been actualized, it is time to heal the wound, and change the story."

"I guess blame has no place."

He said, "Blame *does* have a place, an essential place. Long-harbored blame toward others or self, enables a story to cement and perpetuate. From this story, we are catalyzed to fulfill a (for lack of a better word), *soulic* intent. When that intent is achieved, that particular story—ends. Blame (which cemented the story) is expelled. Releasing blame, at first, feels foreign, much like having a dream you thought was real and realizing it was just a dream. This distancing from a story enables forgiveness and the prospect of a new adventure. These rich stories and all the characters in them are woven together, bright and dark, to create the tapestry of life."

"So, when the story ends, then the Core Wound heals."

"Yes. But if we consciously choose to end a story because we are tired of the plot, it helps to understand the nature of the Core Wound. Understanding why the story is, and from where the story sprung, enables us to make a leap toward ending undesired patterns of behavior."

I nodded, wanting very much to end my martyr-victim behavior. I was aware then of the trickling sound of the cavern stream flowing. I sighed under its soothing influence. The simple thought of taking control of my life always felt so good.

I said, "I guess it is really all about facing ourselves."

"Yes," He replied, "You can see then why repressing, forgetting, and denying the Core Wound are but temporary fixes to ease the symptoms but not the ailment. Even positive thinking, when used to cover underlying truths, can hinder more than help. You can think positively, 'My husband is not cheating on me.' But if he is— he is. You can rip off the head of the weed, but the roots grow it back. You can say, 'Everything's great. Everything's fine.' Still, deep down inside, the wound is as fresh as the day you received it, perhaps eons ago, and negative emotions remain easily triggered."

"Positive thinking can be helpful though, right?"

"Seeing beauty in hard situations is fruitful. Finding a gift in tragedy, and a treasure in garbage—is fruitful. But using positive thinking to actualize a conscious desire can be less rewarding."

"What do you mean?"

"We might find we are not happy with what we wished for—and received. For instance, while willing your house to sell without a hitch might yield desired results, the results might actually divert you from a better prize that your unconscious knows you need. Perhaps the deal to sell your house would serve you better if it fell through, because there is a better offer down the road."

I nodded. "I see."

He continued, "Or, the prize might appear negative, such as: the sale failed and now you are stuck in your house and you are tired of trying to sell it. Yet this failed sale might lead to hidden riches, such as dealing with anger and disappointment that spotlights deeper issues within you that need healing. For example, 'I want to sell my house so I can get away from my parents nagging ways.' A delay in selling might force you to make a stand with your parents to guard your boundary by raising self respect." He raised His brows. "Self respect . . . pretty big prize, yes?"

I stretched my shoulders to my ears to get out the kinks, and then relaxed with a heavy exhale. "So, mind power is real, but we might want to be careful how we use it."

He added, "When you take instruction from your conscious mind, it can run you into circles and dead ends. Consciousness is so often ignorant when it stands alone, cut off from its center of all-knowing wisdom, the underground stream flowing to and fro Pure Creative Energy, to and fro time and timelessness, separation and connection, shadow and light. Say to yourself, 'All is well on the grand scale, even if the binocular view looks bad. All will work out in the end, even if it seems impossible. Whatever happens, then that is what is best for me.' "

I raised my brows. "So, thinking brightly in a broader sense, actually serves us better than imposing our will to attain what we *think* we want."

He nodded. "When we impose our will obstinately to obtain certain objectives no matter what, we damn our natural flow. Such blocking can result in missed opportunities to deal with better or even less desirable circumstances, which can build backbone, expand compassion, inspire creative thinking, widen vision, and so much more. You can win by using your will, but you can lose by winning. You can get the guy to love you, but maybe that guy will do you wrong. A more balanced use of the mind might be, 'Whatever is right for me or another, beyond my conscious understanding—let it be. Whoever I am deep down, whatever I am meant to be—I trust that unfolding.' In this sense, one gives themselves over to their own grand design instead of fighting it. One believes in their own unique way of blossoming rather than trying to control the outer world around them."

I nodded. "It's like, whatever kind of flower you are, embrace it. If you are a daisy, be a daisy and bring out those gifts, instead of trying to be a carnation, or a buttercup."

He smiled. "Flowery analogy, but I like it."

"What a relief to think that way," I said. "Whoever we are, whatever we are, is distinctively beautiful."

"Yes, and imagine if you made yourself appear and act like a buttercup and fooled everyone into believing you are; what are you missing by not being a daisy?"

"Yes," I said, "I can see how using mind energy to make something happen, instigated by conscious perception, can be shortsighted. What about negative thinking? What happens with that?"

He replied, "Seeing only the negative is also a trap, attracting frictional energies to come into play. Fear attracts what you—fear. However, if you are afraid, then instead of decisive positive thinking, envision yourself balanced within. This will disengage you from outside currents. If you fear you won't make the drive home safely, but trust what you have designed for yourself, you will have an impulse that insists, "I will make it home." And you will. Conversely, the impulse might make you aware that an event is about to happen as a catalyst *for your own unfolding*, and prepare you instead. Harsh events are not always as bad as they seem.

Every difficult event brings a gift. Accepting the gift can bring great reward and long-term relief."

"I see," I said. "We live more fully when we allow Creative Energy to flow unimpeded by our perceptions. Instead of pushing for what we desire, flow with our heart, and whatever comes, ride each wave to the fullest. Like you always say, 'Live with Gusto!' "

I couldn't view His face very well, but I bet He was smiling.

He said, "Yes. And if one consciously decides to end a pattern, living in this manner makes it easier to locate the Core Wound, for it is not covered in denial, wishful thinking, or ignorance." He rose. "Come, I will demonstrate." He walked back toward the massive web, purple robe glimmering.

I rose and hobbled behind Him.

He returned to where I'd found Him sitting on the bulge of cavern rock and gestured for me to sit next to Him. I felt like we were sitting on a cavern bench, feet touching the ground.

"Look upon the web."

In the company of abundant burning candles, I looked upon the ghostly glowing web. It was thick, so thick.

He said, "Consciously ending unwanted patterns, or worn out ways of being, such as many failed relationships, ongoing financial trouble, or perpetual victimization, requires three steps. 1: Locating the Core Wound 2: Owning the Core Wound, and 3: Changing conclusions derived at the wounds inception."

I stared at My Fool's silhouette, all wise like Father Time. "So, how is this done?"

He looked at me, eyes reflecting candlelight. It seemed like the flames were talking to me. "It begins with self-awareness. Once you discover a pattern to your pain, you will have a clue about the nature of the Core Wound."

"Like how?" I asked.

He replied, "If, for instance; you always get emotional when a man overrides you, then you know your Core Wound involves an inability to deal with the male nature. Knowing this, you might in the future, be able to discern the past from the present. For instance: a man cuts in front of you at the department store check-out counter. You want to run and hide. That vulnerable feeling resurrects memories of when other men overpowered you. Knowing that the man who cut in front of you has nothing to do with the men of your past, changes your current awareness. Instead of running and hiding, you might sternly say, 'Excuse me, I was in line first.' Pain from the past begins to fade because you have empowered yourself in ways you once could not. In this way, you actually change the past by changing the present. The web is less dense. The Core Wound is less camouflaged."

My eyes widened. "That incident actually happened to me."

His eyes sparkled. "I know."

Gee, what *didn't* He know?

He said, "Once you get better at being aware of the obvious wounds that reinforce your current unwanted behavior, you will begin to learn the fine art of expanding to the overview."

"In what way?"

"For instance, you see a father slap his child. This saddens you deeply. You feel like hiding in a closet. You have a memory flash of your father hitting you. You felt worthless. Now enlarge the picture. Move outside yourself as the child and see the greater scene. You might see that your dad was drinking heavily, and the slap sent you across the room. Your previous conclusion changes. 'I was slapped by my father not because I was unworthy, but because dad was an alcoholic.' Now ascend from the scene, higher still. From there you can view the incident of being slapped as a tiny scene in the greater picture. You might see that you'd been assaulted by your father many times, but that time was the last straw. That was the time you decided you were not worthy. Now look at the scenes around you of your life all playing side by side. You will see how these scenes highlight your feelings of unworthiness: not getting picked for the school play, your lover cheating on you, not being selected for the job, getting mugged, having a best friend betray you, an auto accident, being sued, going bankrupt. Everything that happens confirms your belief that you are unworthy. This belief will cause you to develop behaviors to survive, such as 'hiding from life,' 'staying in the background,' and 'silencing your true feelings.' From an aerial view, you would see how you have perpetuated this, which is the first step to ending the pattern."

The cavern stream sounded louder and more beautiful. It seemed when one comes face to face with the heart of a matter, everything seems bolder and more real.

He continued, "If your nature were more warrior-like, then a different conclusion and set of events might have ensued. For example: 'I'm all right, it is others who are unworthy. Fathers are demons, and men are bad. I will get them before they get me.' You are the one doing the suing, and the rejecting. The belief that others are unworthy caused you to develop a highly offensive personality. Your belief could get so twisted that you harm others. Yet again, if you could see the aerial view, the maze of your life would be revealed. You would see the Core Wound that initiated your strife. You would see how your strife unfolded a great story. You would see that to conclude the story, you must heal the Core Wound."

I asked, "Can one heal the Core Wound from the overview?"

"One can begin healing there, but finish it by going inside the wound, for only there can we be at the moment of its inception, and only from the moment, can we dissolve it as if it never was. Only then can we reap the benefits of the wound, but release the painful memories that came with it."

"Can you give an example?"

He said, "An abandoned baby grows up angry at the world. If she could see her life from an overview, she would witness how this Core Event created a Core Wound that catalyzed her to forge a particular path. In her case, her path might be to show the world that she is somebody important, and thus become an Olympic skier. Seeing that her achievement would never have been, had she not been born with rough beginnings, enables her to release the disdain she has harbored regarding those beginnings. Retained suffering is released. The Core Wound begins to heal, and her current life is less stressful, for she has begun to make peace with the world, and herself. Yet to keep the anger from recurring, she must go into the moment of the wounds inception."

"How?" I said.

He rose and walked close to the middle of His web and faced me, as if on stage to perform. "You must jump the linear thread, and go to the intent of the story before it began."

"So, getting there is more of a meditation, rather than reviewing every incident that ever happened to us?"

"Yes." He gazed into my eyes, in a hypnotic way. "Shifting focus from here to there, happens in moments. You need not know when or where the first stone was thrown to locate the Core Wound. Find a quiet place and be still. Zero in on your most frequent worst feeling. It might be rage, guilt, sorrow, or something you can't describe. The feeling will be flavored with something that is uniquely you, like a feeling that turns your guts, or a particular guilt that haunts you. Don't think about what causes that feeling. Just sit with the feeling. Look within yourself. See a tunnel. Travel into the tunnel and see where you come out. You will come out inside a wound. Wherever you land, trust that. You may or may not have landed in the Core Wound. It does not matter. If you don't locate the first stone thrown, it is not your time, nor your failing. Where you land is what needs addressing. Healing any wound can alter your current story, even if it can't end it so that you can begin a new one. Still, you will feel better, and your story will unfold as designed."

I felt drawn into the experience, and on some level, I was following His instructions.

He continued, "Once inside the wound, you will experience the conclusion you drew when first wounded. For instance: The woman abandoned at birth might revisit her Core Wound by experiencing her birth and the lack of warm reception. She can now behold her initial unconscious reaction, 'I feel unsafe. I am alone. Survival is up to me. The world is a hard, cruel place.' While these initial conclusions motivated her life story: growing up angry, developing arrogance, and obsessed with proving her worth, *reliving*, not remembering, the Core Event that caused the Core Wound, dissolves the old conclusions that have kept the wound from healing. Now, new conclusions can be made. 'I am safe in my heart. I belong in the human family. Humans can help each other. The world has a bright side. I have always been important. My rough beginnings were a gift. I was abandoned at birth so that I would be motivated to become an Olympic Skier.' These new conclusions will serve to end an old pattern, and initiate a new story in her life."

"So," I said, she still *had* the life with anger, but by revisiting the Core Wound, she detaches from it with a wiser knowing, and the anger is dissolved as if it never was."

"Yes! She went back and changed the conclusions born from the moment of inception." His eyes seemed to smile at me.

I still felt entranced. Shaking myself out of it a little, I said, "Do you know what your Core Wound is about?"

He nodded. "It occurred before this current time. Pacifism caused my downfall. After that, I was birthed into a series of life-time experiences where I was compelled to control and conquer. Passive people annoyed me, seeming weak. Yet controlling-type people annoyed me too, for in my ancient passivity, I had once been their victim. I had to be in control—always. Once I move into this wound and heal it, I will understand the beauty and power in passivity. My need to conquer will fade. I will have taken responsibility for what I created. I *am* the spider that created the web."

"Wow!" I exclaimed. "I want to do that. I want to find my Core Wound and end my martyr-victim pattern."

"It will happen naturally, but if you choose to facilitate ending the pattern, set the intent, and be open for the right time, which might be now, or maybe later in dreams, or between waking and sleep, or moments when your facade is not strong." His voice was gentle, so gentle. "If you say, the experience must be like this or that, or right now, then your mind is not open. When you open your mind to how and when an unwanted pattern can end, you invite unexpected experiences to facilitate that ending. It might occur in the flash of a second: a vision, an understanding, a release. Or it might span time and end bit by bit through a succession of enlightening experiences."

"Stay open-minded," I echoed.

"Open-mindedness leads to pleasantly surprising occurrences and choices. One's story can still be lived, but with an awareness that what is being lived is a story. In this, your reactions will be altered. Your story will have new dimension, and the way you experience the story will change. "

I realized then that I had been attempting to do precisely that. My life overwhelmed me. I needed change. "I struggle," I gulped back a cry, "to experience my life story with new insight."

"You *are*. You are learning not to react to chaos with the belief that existence is brutal. You are learning to dip under the raucous waves, instead of being carried away or smashed by them."

"I get it. I am changing the way I handle what comes at me." Quite suddenly, I sensed the event that was my first stone thrown in my current story. It involved denouncing all confrontation, conflict, dissension, anger, and even irritation. I wondered what Core Event could trigger the belief that I didn't even have the right to be irritated. What *was* this Core Event? How was the wound created? What were my conclusions? I was excited to melt those conclusions, break the pattern, and change my life. "I suppose my Core Wound has something to do with my obsession for warriors."

He nodded. "You outcast the warrior part of *you*, Susan. The warrior, for you, is your male aspect. You outcast the male aspect of yourself. And you've been trying to get him back ever since."

A vision played in my mind. "I see a place, not seeming to be earth really." I sneered. "I feel like I am making this up."

"It doesn't matter," He said, "in a way, everything is made up. This isn't about true or false, everything is true and everything is false. Glean the gist of the experience. If your wedding ring went down the drain and you can't remember how, but it had something to do with a fight when you lost your temper, does it matter if you lost your temper in France or England? Does it matter if you were wearing jeans or a dress? Continue, Susan. Sink into the energy of the situation."

I sighed hard and gathered courage. "I misused my power, resulting in great destruction. To repent, I shunned that power, along with the ability to protect myself. Since then, I've tried to get others to protect me."

"Precisely. This was how you set up exploring the martyr-victim theme in the earth story. To conclude that exploration, you must make peace with its beginning. When retained emotion from that Core Wound is released, then the current martyr-victim theme (which stands on the foundation of that wound) also falls. Others who choose to experience the martyr-victim energy will continue the theme or story you leave behind. In a way, all the stories play on. Only the players change by defocusing from one story, and focusing on another. Everything is happening at once, but where is your focus? Where your focus lies, so does your life experience."

I felt an ominous presence behind me. I turned around slowly. A huge black spider hung in the air on a gossamer strand of silk attached to a massive cobweb on the cave ceiling. My web, I was guessing. I had the oddest feeling the spider was staring into my eyes. Its thin black legs chilled me.

He said, "You are the creator of your web, not a thing to be hated, but appreciated, understood, and released."

I stepped back. "Creator or not, I'm not ready to deal with *this* thing yet."

"Few can accept all that they have created." He approached me from behind, arriving at my side.

I responded without looking at Him, watching the eight-legged thing. "You fear the spider too?"

"I do. But my fear differs from yours. You fear aggression. I fear vulnerability. I could not look at you when you walked into this room. You would see what I labor to cut out of me, weakness in any form. Consequently, I become the hard driver, stern and unyielding toward accomplishing an end, no matter what the goal. The desire for illumination fades into my desire for victory. Yet, all that we shun comes back to us through other people who poke at the Core Wound that is merely covered, not healed."

"So, we have to accept the spider, the creator of our life experience, is us. We must find beauty in it, if we are to find beauty in ourselves."

He nodded. "All our life events are spawned from this spider."

The spider came toward me. I stiffened, preparing to flee.

"Do not run," He said.

The spider moved to my shoulder and crawled up my neck.

I squeezed my eyes shut. "Oh, get this thing off me!"

He said, "You feel invaded by this spider? The spider is you."

My heart pounded. How could I remain casual and listen to His words while this spider was crawling toward my cheek! The spider crawled up the side of my head, light skinny legs tickling with each step. I felt hysterical. I started to whimper.

He continued, "Your wound was inflicted by a part of you that felt it deserved punishment. You attract others to manifest that belief. A person who believes suffering is divine, will *unconsciously* invite assault. A person who believes there is no love, chases love away, snapping and snarling at all the would-be lovers until they flee. A person that believes everyone else is inferior, may conquer the world to prove that she is not!"

The spider crawled on top of my head. I wanted to scream.

He said, "You create circumstances to experience them. Accept that. You can change those circumstances if you choose. Accept that. If you are soul worn from being a martyr—stop. If I am finished being a tyrant, I will stop. The answer is the same, whether you are the bully or the bullied. Integrate your shadow self."

My body was constricted. I could not breathe. I don't know how, but the spider started crawling into my brain.

His voice sounded far away. "Accept your worth."

I rambled frantically, "I'm worthy! I'm worthy!"

His voice echoed from further and further away. "Accept your warrior."

"I am a warrior," I shouted, "but I attack myself!"

"Use the warrior to defend yourself."

"I don't do that."

"And I—too much."

As I accepted that I created my own reality, I felt the spider fade into me, not so much an invasion anymore. I swallowed hard.

He surprised me with a chuckle and touched my shoulder. "The more you slam yourself, the more you might get slammed. The more you believe the world cheated you, the more you might cheat the world. To end that, release blame and embrace self."

"I get it," I said, finally relaxing. "It is like any minority—be it appearance, race, creed, color, or socio-economic status—cannot achieve position by slamming the majority. Only by embracing their own worth, do they rise from the rubble. Likewise, the majority can easily vilify any minority for their problems. Yet, no matter how much a minority is crippled or eradicated, the problems never cease, because the majority won't embrace the part of themselves that is represented in the minority they are rejecting." I exhaled hard. That made a lot of sense when I was saying it, but I'm not sure it sounded sensible.

"What is sensible?" He said, reading my mind again. "You've tapped into something. What else do you want to say?"

Words emerged from somewhere inside me, a place that had roots into the world. I spoke, unsure of what I was going to say until I said it. "When the industrial revolution exploded, many tribal peoples who represented oneness with land and nature, were used and abused. Progress couldn't mushroom if we valued the natural state of the land, the purity of the oceans, and the cleanliness of the air. Progress was the priority. Mountains of dirt and rock were gouged for mountains of currency. Homegrown food, or food by community trade was replaced with the modernized grocery store. Synthetic drugs slowly replaced nature's medicine. What was natural within us was overthrown by the wonders of machines, and the dictates of an industrial society. Of course, the peoples whose heritage centered on living harmoniously with nature would be demeaned. Of course, their great oppression would begin, for had it not begun in us? Had we not begun to repress that part of us that would run naked in the wind, and crave apples instead of candy? Had we not already begun to devalue our own instincts and worship the image? Our irreverence to the natural earth correlated with our irreverence toward tribal people."

He smiled. "You are finding your song, the song of Susan. You don't need others to tell you what your song is, not even me. The greatest gift you can receive is the gift you give yourself. People generally underestimate their ability to tap wisdom, but it is at the fingertips of all, this deep fathomless pool of insight."

I smiled warmly. He was an unusual sage, ever turning me inward to myself, in addition to the wisdom He shared.

He grasped my shoulders gently, and turned me in a circle. The cave walls had pictures, like petroglyphs of all I disliked: violence, cruelty, and the baser parts of human existence. He said, "Look at what frightens or enrages you. Then with full heart . . . absorb it. Make it part of you. Reclaim what you shun."

I gulped. "Not appealing."

"Yet," He said, "not appealing—yet."

My resistance was strong, but my quest for completeness was stronger. I began breathing deeply, inhaling the essence of each petroglyph. And it hurt. The walls of my good, sweet person image were hailed with bullets propelled by primitive energy. I kept assuming I was beyond that image. Sometimes you can't tell how far you've come until you're actually under attack.

My knees buckled and smacked the cavern floor. It hurt.

He said, "You are always the victim. Why? You deplete yourself by giving endlessly to those who can't respond. Why? Let the warrior rise inside you, Susan. Let the warrior enter your rainbow world. Integrate what you fear: anger, aggression, and confrontation. Give yourself the power to fight back."

I felt the hunters, the soldiers, the authoritarians tearing apart my idea of love. Would my heart explode? Agony burst upward from the depths of my being. I did not want to do this thing! "This might destroy me!"

"Says the pacifist." His hands hovered over my head, feeling oddly like the spider that had been there. His tone lowered, "Develop the warrior within yourself. Then you will be free from his tyranny."

I started sobbing deeply, but silently. If I were brave enough, I could harness the warrior's powers. This meant I could save myself. I wouldn't have to rely on a man, or ever be at a man's mercy again. Yes, I wanted that. I was willing to put up my dukes and fight. At long long last . . . I was. For a natural born pacifist, that was a big step. My heart pounded as a small vision played before me. The sword Excalibur rose from the water, gripped by the Lady of the Lake. I realized clearly how every life required surviving a battle that presents us with opportunities to know ourselves. We are pushed to the brink of our being, and behold, a star is born. We embrace the magic of the Universe, the miracle of blood and breath, and the reality of all things imagined.

He gave a faint laugh. "The reality of all things imagined, indeed. Oh, what an adventure—this life."

A tornado force whirled above my head descending over my body. The force was enormous, mightier than I ever imagined. I cried to Him, "Hold on to me!"

His hand pressed on my head. "Enough for now." The tornado energy faded. "You are not ready for more."

I panted hard, feeling like I'd failed again.

He helped me stand. "You did not fail. Allow yourself to unfold naturally. Embrace these small steps. They will take you far."

I wiped away my tears.

"I take small steps too." He gazed upon the silvery strands of His web. His voice dripped rich with feeling. "This day of days, I approached the wounds involving my birth mother. She tried to control me passively, using guilt to imprison me into her reality. I was told she would die if I did not behave. This angered me. I unconsciously projected my anger onto my father, and rebelled against him, because after all, if I rebelled against my mother, she would die, right? I have resented the passive aggressive personality, for it roped me into behaving against my instincts. I can't in good conscious throw punches, or assert my will when such a person pleads. Therefore, I must surrender to them. If only the passive aggressive would directly throw a punch, I could punch back. But they don't, they never do."

I said, "That's because they fear your reactions and don't dare provoke you, lest they be pummeled. And they would be, right?"

"Alas, that is so. I just dislike seeing it, because then I must see myself and place my anger where it belongs, at my own inability to stand against guilt. Then, because I give into it, my individuality is threatened. My freedom is threatened. Then, I'm more controlling in other ways to compensate. Why does this happen? This answer that I have already shared with you was found in the Core Event that elicited the Core Wound. I have discovered much about why preserving my eccentricity has been so imperative, and the price I have paid to do so. Once I enter the Core Wound, my barriers will come down, and I will face what I fear. Old repetitive patterns of conquering and shielding will be released."

"Then, we both have yet to move into our Core Wound?"

"Yes." He reached down to the cavern floor and grabbed the paper He had been writing on. He walked away toward the tunnel that led out of the cavern room. Then He turned and faced me. He had folded the paper into an airplane and sailed in the air toward me. "Ain't—Life—Great!"

The paper landed at my feet, and He watched as I picked it up.

A blood-red stone was nestled in the white folds. "The Gem of Strife," He said. "Bullets and blades cannot rip the soul like daggered words and acts of betrayal. And yet, without such wounds, how limited our experience would be. Oh what roads have we traveled in the name of attaining honor, or seeking vengeance?"

I held the crimson gem that burned my palm, not too unbearably. I said, "The Gem of Strife then, gives us the drama we seek. And in that drama, we bleed, learning about hate and pain—and consequently, love and healing."

He said, "Pain and healing, one coin, two sides."

When I looked up at Him, He had vanished into the darkness of the tunnel.

"Goodbye," I murmured. My time with Him was never enough. I placed the stone reverently in my pack with the others. I picked up the paper and straightened the folds, beholding the written word. I looked to the tunnel again where He'd disappeared. I wondered where I might meet Him next. A Core Wound?

I went to where He'd been sitting, where the light was brightest. I sat in front of the massive white spider web and read the paper.

It said, "This day of days, deep wounds sucked this self into anger, judgment, and an attempt to orchestrate people's lives. This self slid backwards, tangled in the past and future."

I paused a moment, grasping the intensity of My Fool's pain. .

I continued reading the paper. "Do not follow each web strand, for the strands go on forever leading to paths of blame that catch one as a fly in passing. Rather, discover the whole web at once by beholding the Core Wound that elicited all the spinning. This self wove the web. Judgment of self and others are subjective. We all have experiences. We all have intrinsic worth. We are all one great self that seeks to curiously explore and create. See the web for what it is, and not the fragments of what it has become."

I sighed, nodding. We so often judge everything from the fragments we see. Seeing the overview, sheds new light.

I read on. "When this self can release the retained emotion that keeps the Core Wound in existence, then the whole wound, the whole web will dissolve. That theme, that particular story will be over, and a new one can begin. Free self. There is only one freedom, and that is from our own oppression. Then for whom is the call of calls, calling? Is it not calling for this self?"

Yes, I thought. The greatest call really is to our own self. The large self calls for the small self to come home, and the small self calls to the large self for rescue. Some people call the large self, God. However, I could see now that the idea of any God is still a concept. And the large self engulfs all concepts.

His struggle coursed through my body. I read to the end. "This self has recovered from a challenging bump in the road. There will be others, but recovery is easier each time. Then one day, in the blink of an eye, no more bumps. The story ends in beauty."

Tears dribbled down my cheeks. He had shared His struggle with me. I was touched, for He, the controller, world conqueror, rebel to those who tread too near . . . trusted me. He had made Himself vulnerable. He had changed by touching His wound and realizing its source. Here, in this inner world, He claimed no fame, knowledge, or truth. He flowed right out of the Cave of Wounds on Pure Creative Energy—a magic carpet that transcended all stories.

Then all my insights came together: Illumination was achieved by being fluid, loosening the glue that cements wounds, salted with the perception of blame. Blaming locks in pain. Gathering courage to see beyond the clouds that hide beginnings reveals that pain is felt when it is accepted. It is accepted to create a story, to have an experience. When one desires a story to end, then and only then will the last page be turned.

What is missing in us that we expect others to fulfill? What is hurting in us that we expect others to fix? No one can fill us. No one can fix us. Sooner or later, everyone realizes that we can only fill and fix ourselves, and only when we are ready. Only we can clear our own web away, for it was we who wove it.

Then I had an epiphany about behaviors I'd developed due to my Core Wound. 'Because I feel undeserving, I don't stand up for myself. I don't make myself seen, therefore I am not noticed. I am prone to see only love and light, and predators take advantage.' I decided to change these old ways with a new affirmation. 'I am worthy! I am a radiant being. I can't be talked out of my embracing my worth.' By seeing my shadow, I saw myself. Oh, I knew I still had to visit the Core Wound, but just sensing it and the impact it had on my life, was already changing me.

As John Muffet once wrote, "Little Miss Muffet, sat on a tuffet, eating her curds and whey, along came a spider, who sat down beside her, and scared poor Miss Muffet away!" If Miss Muffet returned, she'd realize that what scared her was her shadow self, which is the part of her she fears to face. That dark side in each of us harbors all the ugly things we'd rather not claim. However, in claiming what we deem ugly, we find unexpected beauty.

Now it's your turn. Where is your spider web? Everyone has one, hidden or not, it is there. It *is* there. How expansive is your Core Wound? How large is the web? How many life experiences have stemmed from this wound? How deep does it go?

If you feel truly ready to end an unwanted life pattern, play music that inspires. Go to or visualize a scene of natural beauty that arouses your deeper being. Journey within yourself, like moving into a tunnel. Harbor the intent to discover and heal a Core Wound that catalyzed the story you wish to conclude that you may begin a new one. When you exit the tunnel, you will be in the Core Wound. Don't question it. Behold your feelings, and your thoughts. What conclusions did you draw? See how these conclusions motivated your story. Allow Creative Energy to flow inside the wound, lending insight. Replace the old conclusions with these new insights. With these new insights, we write the last page of an old story and begin the first page of a new one. Oh what chronicles we have written! And in beholding that we are the creator of all our realities, a note of music rises from the mystery.

Hear that note? That single note that becomes a symphony calling, "It is I. It is I. It is I. Don't you know who I am?" And in the single act of listening, you behold the Universe. Blink your eyes. When you open them again, you will have stars in *your* hands.

Walking the Mine Field

"You can't be happy where you're not,
If you're not happy where you're at."

GEM #7 LOVE

I stared at the enormous web above me. My stomach gurgled. I was
nervous. Had I truly created all that? According to Him, if I climbed
to the core, I would discover the reason for my pain, see the whole
web, and great understanding would arrive. However, I'd learned
to distrust my physical eyes and conscious evaluation of matters,
knowing how illusive they could be. So before I began the climb, I
had to look inward. Looking inward is easy if you draw down the
shades. I closed my eyes.

I posed the question. "What do humans search for? And why is
the need to attain it so great we are willing to suffer in our pursuit?
What prize motivates us to traverse the maze of earth existence?"

He answered in my mind. I was getting used to Him replying
to me in this manner. "We call this prize many things: power,
status, success, worth, and acknowledgment, but most commonly,
it's called love. All our actions circle back to the need to feel significant by getting others to deem us important. We tend to discount
our own proclamation of significance, keeping it dormant until
another declares it first. We seem to require validation, hence—
drama. The search for this validation, this confirmation that we are
worth loving, goes on. And on. And on."

I viewed my own search. I had spun more strands on the web
life after life, expanding outward, getting further away from the
source of my identity's creator—me. Me as Pure Creative Energy. I
had become the rind and forgotten the core. I knew light, but I had

forgotten what it felt like to be the sun.

He answered in my head again, "All a part of the plot, my dear. The human race has distanced itself from its own creative core. A popular science fiction plot is that machines attain human will. The scarier and more realistic event is that humans become robots. In a certain regard, many have. But just as a leaf in the wind, one can only last so long without connection to the branch, which is connected to the trunk, the roots, the whole tree."

A chill shot through my body. Suddenly I felt an urgency to get consciously reconnect to the trunk *of being* before I was lost forever. But how?

He said telepathically, "Identities, as designed, have forgotten they are One. Believing that we are separate from each other sets into motion wild exciting stories, fictions that we call reality. But now we have spun off so far into the fiction that we struggle to breathe, because the air supply is in totality. We begin to fall apart, searching frantically for what will put us back together, for what will make us feel like we belong, and for what will make us feel like we are okay, and the world is okay. This is an unconscious attempt to again experience Oneness."

It suddenly occurred to me why a general apathy seemed to be infecting the human race. With the advent of the mass media, our sense of self was increasingly affected by the giant social world around us, clouding our core being. Our quintessence had dimmed. And in this dimming, this disconnection from the roots that feed life, a natural yearning burgeons. A yearning to come 'alive' again, to feel bright again, to tap the inner sanctum of who we are, apart from what the social world has led us to believe. By disengaging from the reflection of the masses, we tap our individuality. Individuals, like puzzle pieces that form into original shapes, can connect with each other, experiencing a greater picture. This would be as breathing some Pure Creative Energy back into the illusion of separation. I thought of Martin Luther King, and Gandhi. As strong individuals not adhering to conformity, they catalyzed great connections amongst others.

My Fool spoke in my mind. "Cycles. Breathe out—separation. Breathe in—totality."

Yes, that was it. I needed to inhale and take myself back from the reflection. I needed to come home—to me. Though my physical body appeared stationary, inwardly I walked the web strands, heading toward the center. Along the way, I saw people, the selves I used to be, and . . . or—still am, snared in web clumps. A blue-faced corpse had strangled itself from being tangled too tightly. A blistered man writhed and moaned, "Love burns." A middle-aged woman glared at me with foul rancor and uttered, "There is no love." Another prayed, "Someone save me!" Another screamed, "Why can't someone love me?"

Even in the life of Susan, I had cried out such things. Getting to the web's center by crossing every strand would take forever. I had to cut through lateral space and linear time to go back to the first stone thrown.

Another spider dropped before me, helmet-sized, hanging on a strand of web. Its black bulbous eyes seemed to smile and say, "Claim me." This spider seemed to carry more power than the first one that went into my brain. *That* spider was more about accepting that I had created my reality. *This* spider wanted me to be aware of the reality I was creating *now*.

I decided to accept this spider, as I had the first one.

Little legs conducted their way up the strand over my head, then lowered itself inside my brain, filling my body. Creative urges spawned phantom limbs next to my other appendages, giving me more mobility than I'd ever had. I had become spider-like. I wanted to move and weave experiences with Creative Energy. I wanted to *be*. In a split second, I understood why my other selves anguished in the web.

Words flowed from my lips in a trance state. "Thy selves know not true love. They speak   of the need and the desire for *someone else* to fulfill them. They are trapped in the web because they believe love has to be *attained*. What they really seek is the remembrance of totality. Wholeness *is* love. All that exists is One. Thus, our worth is intrinsic. Ego is an illusion because there is no separation. All realities flow through us. We flow through all realities, though our consciousness blots most of our awareness. The common question is, 'Am I worthy of love?' To say no, is to denounce all that exists in life. We usually wait for someone else to validate our worth. Once that is done, we look to that person to maintain it, as if we alone are capable of neither."

I started thinking of how desperately I wanted a powerful warrior to affirm my worth. Why? Why did I want it to come from a warrior? Why? Why? Why!

Suddenly, I was dizzy. Though I felt like a sage in some ways, another part of me was all tripped up inside. Suddenly, I fell downward, floating through sticky strands into the gossamer beginnings of the web's center.

I landed hard in a weed scattered dirt field. Shrill pains shot through the arches of my feet.

I looked down at my boots, worn and dirty.

"I once knew a girl called—" I jumped, turning toward the voice. Of course, it was Him. He was pillowed in a soft red-hooded cape with folds that seemed almost ethereal. His skin glowed pink. He reminded me of a dragon in a J.R.R. Tolkien story.

I swallowed hard, apprehensive of what might happen next. "You're looking . . . magical."

His face sparkled red. He smiled faintly. "Creative Energy will do that to you."

His strange state unnerved me. He seemed too inhuman. I stepped back, wringing my hands. "Is this a Core Wound?"

His head cocked. His eyes had cleared from the fog of sorrow that weighted Him just moments ago in the Cave of Wounds. His pupils flickered mischief. "This is the jumping off point."

I grimaced, a little afraid.

And then, He told me a story in a kind of code. *Feet* symbolized my relationship with myself. *Shoes* symbolized my relationship with others. I didn't have to figure it out. I just knew.

"I once knew a girl called Sue, but she was known to some by other names. When she is close to me in the dream world, I call her Susan, but others have names for her too.

"Once, when she was an infant in her crib, she discovered she had feet. Feet amazed her. As she grew, she joyously explored the many ways she could use her feet: standing, walking, running, kicking, climbing, jumping, squishing mud through her toes, or stepping on a cool wet beach that soothed her soles. Her soul.

"Sometimes her feet would hurt when she'd step on a rock or stub her toes. One day she was given a pair of shoes. They protected her, but they also confined her dear dear feet.

"She grew up, and tried on many shoes. Some fit right at first, but later, hurt her feet. Some hurt her feet at first, but then later fit right. After much searching, she discovered a pair of shoes that brought her great pleasure. They were the most comfortable shoes she had ever worn. Loving the shoes, she decided to keep them forever. She wore them for so long, the shoes got old and started to fall apart. But she didn't want to give them up, so she repaired them. For years, she repaired them. After many adjustments, she started to wonder if they really fit her anymore, or if they even brought her the same comfort as when she first got them. In fact, they'd grown tight and no matter what she did, they would not loosen their grip on her precious feet. Her feet could hardly breathe anymore.

"Why should she suffer? After all, other styles were available. She went through several pairs always wondering if the shoes were as she saw them, or the way she *wanted* to see them. All she knew was that when she saw them, she couldn't make her heart stop feeling a worth that hadn't been felt in ages. The question came to her, 'Would any pair of shoes satisfy me? Would there be a fifth and sixth pair? Were there none that could last me forever?'

"She longed for security. Could security be found in shoes that hid her soles? Soul. She realized then that the answer might be found in removing all shoes and rediscovering her feet. It had been long since she had felt her soles, soul, on the sand or beheld her feet without the influence of shoes. She slipped off the shoes that covered her and began to build a meaningful relationship with her feet as once she did lying in the crib. She let her feet breathe and knew she must learn to love them all over again, for then and only then could she ever truly love any shoes.

"She hadn't ever really loved any shoes before, though she thought she did. She needed shoes to protect her precious feet and make them feel beautiful. She called need, love. But in her obsession with shoes, she forgot to cherish her feet.

"Releasing her shoes, gave her back her feet. Her feet carried the beauty and strength of all the shoes. Her feet had more substance and capacity than she had ever dreamed. She could discover more than she did before she began wearing shoes. Then she might even find a pair of shoes right for her, but she will never forget how to take them off or that the shoes don't direct her feet, but her feet direct her shoes. I once knew a girl called Sue, who released the need for outside security and found it deep within."

Tears stung my face. All my life, I tried to please others in exchange for security. I did not look to myself, though I pretended I did. It's simple to make another the center of our lives, covering ourselves up with them, wearing them, so to speak. In time, we are lost in that person.

His eyes sharpened. "Do you want to know your feet?"

I nodded.

He glanced at my feet. "Remove your shoes."

I sat, pulled off my boots and holey socks, and gazed at my pale grimy feet. I rose, brushing dirt off my ripped and battered jeans.

"Susie." I heard a male voice off to my side.

I turned my head and gasped, breathless. I saw the warrior of my dreams. A gust of wind blew his long, black hair back over his shoulders. He looked charismatic, magical, and strong in his black tee shirt, jeans, and boots. Now, *he* could protect me.

My Fool read my mind and said, "Are you sure?"

I nodded, holding my gaze upon this miraculous vision.

My Fool sighed. "You really have a hard time giving up warriors, don't you?"

"Susie," the warrior called again.

My heart hammered. I looked at the warrior. My hammering heart turned to thunder. His eyes emitted such cool confidence, I thought I might swoon. My romantic heart exploded ecstasy.

My Fool interrupted my oh-so-lovely moment, "You can't be happy where you're not, if you're not happy where you're at."

I forced myself to break my stupor so I could look at My Fool when He talked. When I looked to Him, I jumped. His sharp eyes pierced me with truth. Oh, why? Why now! This was my dream come true! His terse words carried a deadly message. "You are walking the mine field. And your warrior is a mine."

"But he's so . . . beautiful."

"You think he has no weakness, faults, or imperfections?"

I sighed dreamily. "He doesn't appear to have anything wrong with him."

"Neither do the shoes behind the fancy glass case. You don't ever really know until you try them on, but then it's too late. Have you ever had an eternally perfect fit?"

"No, but—"

"—but this could be the one?"

I moaned, because I really wanted him to be *the one.*

My Fool said, "Still searching for shoes, little Susie?"

"Susie," the warrior repeated.

I looked at him, lovelorn. His hand reached for me. Oh, how I craved to take it!

My Fool's voice broke through my trance like a thunderclap. "Look at your feet."

I scowled and looked begrudgingly at my neglected feet.

"Do you care to know your feet . . . or not?"

I glared at My Fool. "Yes, but I want to go with the warrior *so badly.*"

"Go then. Give yourself to him. Let him control you. Let him grip your feet until you can't breathe anymore."

I whimpered and scrunched my face in resistance. "I *cannot* leave him!"

"Then don't."

Don't? Don't? I wished it was that simple. Could I throw away my quest to grow into my full potential? No. My heart pounded. No, I could not. The warrior looked appealing now, but later, I'd wind up abused. I always, always did. No matter how much I hoped a warrior could fulfill my needs, I always wound up oppressed. I swallowed the sorrow of this tortuous goodbye, and turned away from this magnificent warrior who was all I thought I ever wanted.

I pushed myself into a fast walk, abandoning the warrior *and* My Fool. My Fool made me see the truth. I hated My Fool for that. Unfair? Yes, I know. But ugly vehemence welled in me. Ignorance is bliss, they say. I hope not. Not anymore anyway. Not now, when I was well on my way to illumination.

I felt my every step taking me away from the beautiful warrior. I was aware of my every breathe, lungs filling—exhaling. Filling—exhaling. And my heartbeat hurt my ears. Thoughts rolled through me, heightening my sorrow. I wanted a warrior to behave in the ways I felt blocked. I needed him to stand in front of me and face aggression with a cold eye, placing empathy for the enemy on a shelf to defend my honor, and put up his dukes and fight. Developing those abilities in myself would be an enormous task. Enormous beyond imagination. Enormous for me.

Above me, I heard flapping wings. I looked up and saw My Fool in dragon form, red wings streamlined above me. My jaw fell open. I couldn't believe it.

He hollered, "Finding yourself requires great courage."

I didn't want My Fool haunting me just now. I needed time to ditch this truth, too hot for me to bear.

I ran hard, stepping on stones and stickers, hurting my precious feet. I kept glancing up at My Fool's tremendous form that radiated a laser beam intensity aimed at me. I didn't want to hear this truth! I'd left the warrior, but I wasn't ready to find the warrior in me. I just felt that I'd somehow die if I did. I'd die from shame. Warriors were bad, bad, bad! I think My Nun had raised her self-righteous little head in the wave of my denial.

I ran faster.

My Fool flew faster.

The breath from His words singed my hair. "Flow Creative Energy—unimpeded. *Then* you will know freedom. *Then* you will know love. *Then* you will know yourself. Give up the shoes. Give up the shoes and become Susan!"

My bloody feet throbbed with each smack on the raw ground. Didn't He understand how vulnerable I was? Didn't He understand how grossly men used and abused me—for centuries? I don't know how I knew that. I couldn't remember most of the torture, but I certainly carried the scars. My feet needed protection. 'I' needed protection!

He shouted from above, "Protect yourself!"

My breath turned ragged, and my face red. I was tiring. As I slowed, I noticed a strange thing. The field was dotted with warriors, hundreds of them. They all appeared alike, dressed in black, raven hair flowing over sturdy chests. I couldn't stop here, not now. I'd decided to forfeit them, even though I'd be alone and vulnerable in this cruel world. I ran faster, even though my lungs burned, and shrill pains climbed my legs. I ran a long while, but the field never ended and the longhaired warriors were ever-present, staring at me with 'Come, I know you want me' eyes. I could almost feel them beckoning me to scream, 'Save me!'

My feet burned with flamed heat, aching like knife cuts. I could run no more. I fell to my hands and knees, panting breathlessly. How could I resist these warriors? How could I make them go away? Exhaustion undercut my hope. I sobbed in defeat.

My Fool in dragon form landed in front of me, cardinal chest arching. His red webbed wings folded near His body. "Ever hear of the phrase, 'Just say no?' "

I glared at Him, trying to catch my breath. "Just say no?"

"Say no to the warriors without, and yes to the warrior within."

"Just?" I hissed. My tears felt like fire on my face. "*You* try saying no to everything you're parched for!"

He said, "You crave a warrior to love you so dearly that he'll protect you to the death, or maybe even . . . to death?"

"Yes," I said.

"Why," He asked, "so that you will have proof of being loved? And that proof will deem you worthy?"

"Yes," I said softly, ashamed.

He touched my head with a talon, but it felt like all the lost love of the world flushed my face, cooling the torrid heat on my skin. And His words dripped into me. "The love you want from a warrior is not required. Love, defined by humans, is a mirage of the real thing." I sponged His medicinal drops of wisdom, iodine to this protection-infection I'd long perpetuated.

He said, "The music market parades love songs pining for another to love them, aching because somebody won't, joyful because somebody does."

I grumbled, a bit like a two-year old.

His voice was tender, "Why can't the person you love be yourself? Why can't you love yourself, even if no one else does?"

When He said that, I felt a brief communion with myself.

He said, "Why can't *you* be the self that you can't live without? Demeaning yourself until affirmation from another is received, makes you love sick."

"Is that what this is all about? Love sickness, I mean? Is it fed when we run from ourselves?"

He nodded.

I sighed hard. He was right. I truly didn't want Him to be, but He was. I sat back on my knees. "I'm sorry I vented my frustration on you. Taking responsibility for myself is hard."

He half-laughed. "You think getting another to assume responsibility for you is easier?"

I guess it wasn't. And even if others tried, it usually angered me. Who wants to be bound by the laws of another? "I get your point, but it's hard," I said, "to own everything that ever happened to me."

"You think blaming others is easier? Does that yield results?"

I guess it didn't. As long as I made others responsible for my unhappiness, I was powerless. "Taking myself back is difficult," I said, "I've been giving myself away for so long."

"You think taking yourself back is difficult? Would taking another reward you more?"

I guess it wouldn't, because really all I wanted from another anyway was for them to give me back to me. When we feel loved by someone, we come alive. Why must we wait for another to signal our rise to joy? If we can feel our worth then, why can't we feel it anytime? I wrung my hands. "It is just so hard to give ourselves what we seek in another."

"What is hard, and what is not, is dictated by your own command." His human form returned slowly as He spoke, as if showing me the ease of obeying one's own command. "You struggle because you want what you *think* you don't have. And that's how your problems began in the first place. Self-doubt. But you do have what you need. We may derive comfort and security from others, and fear losing it. Or we can have a good relationship with ourselves, where comfort and security are eternal. In this, our relationships with others will also improve."

And though I agreed with Him, the warriors neared me bit by bit like a shrinking donut, and I the hole, getting tinier and tinier as seconds lapsed into the belly of oblivion.

"Why do they still come?" I asked, "I am willing to let them go."

"If you truly were, then go . . . they would. You still broadcast, not consciously, but deep inside—you do."

"Broadcast?"

"When we need affirmation of our worth, then that need is broadcast to the public. We cast our line, baited with sexual energy, into the sea of romantic love. That sexual energy transmits the radar waves of our need throughout the dark, lonely world with the message, 'Meet my need. Sex is your reward.' While bars and night clubs are prime for advertising such needs, the fishing expedition takes place anywhere and everywhere."

I eyed my longhaired army closing in like the *Night of the Living Dead*. "So, I emanate an offer of sex, for love?"

"And to you, love is . . . "

"Protection," I said.

He tapped His finger contemplatively on His chin. "Hmm, reminds me of a young French woman trailing a warrior in England. The warrior turns around to her with a hard questioning face. The woman speaks, 'I give you want you want, I follow?' "

I sucked in a breath of realization, hand flying over heart. "I am still doing it! I had thought that my nun-like nature was my major challenge. But, this doesn't feel nun-like."

"The 'nun' is your hiding place. She is where you go when protection from a man cannot be found. But if you think protection can be found, then you seek attention from the protector outside yourself. The world over, humans seek the attention from others that they will not give to themselves, thus creating great—"

I finished his sentence, "—stories."

He nodded. "Love *is* a popular theme. Getting attention, seeking approval, searching for love—what would a story be, absent these motivators? Coupling is top priority for most. A natural urge to connect ensures procreation and a measure of comfort that unconsciously reminds us of the wholeness we once knew. Coupling revives our sense of 'home.' Families and societies coalesce. This compelling desire for attention, approval, and love . . . is the way it is supposed to be."

"So," I said, "we reach out to replace a sense of loss, born from the *impression* that we are single identities, separated from the whole?"

He nodded. "We emanate our needs, and the call is answered. In your case, you have always wanted to be loved by a warrior who will protect you. Your need has attracted warrior men who desired to be loved by a woman who will submit her power to him in worship. For you, that is attraction, or being in love. The folly in love arrangements is that if either person fails to love us the exact way we want to be loved, the relationship falters."

I nodded. "My husband gets grumpy with me if I don't behave like a Donna Reed type of wife and mother."

"Yes, and you get grumpy when he won't behave like the Sir Lancelot of your dreams."

I nodded, feeling a bit shameful. Perhaps my expectation of him was as unfair as his expectation of me.

A green grasshopper landed on My Fool's shoulder, staring at me strangely. This grasshopper thing kept recurring. I wondered what that meant, but not now. Back to love. "Can another ever fulfill us?"

He laughed. "For a time . . . perhaps, to an extent . . . maybe. But it is not another's job to fulfill us. Others are but players in our story, mirroring something we possess in ourselves. One who represses sensitivity is likely attracted to a sensitive person. One who represses assertiveness is likely attracted to an assertive person. These attractions obviously serve a purpose; however, the purest fulfillment is attained from the journey within. When we journey within, we move into a natural flow. This flow, like a river, like all rivers, moves into the sea of oneness. We simply have a hard time getting ourselves to do it. It is easier and feels more normal to reach outward to find another who will do the job, like Tom Sawyer getting someone else to whitewash the fence."

I was a little afraid the grasshopper would jump on me, and just as I thought that, it sprung at my chest. My eyes blasted open.

The creature landed on my heart, clutching a rip on my blue shirt. He was soft and sweet, kind of, just sitting there like a friend.

My saucer eyes did not distract My Fool. His speech strolled on without disruption, though I think I missed a sentence. "Letting people off the hook to sate your need, means putting away your fishing rod. It means meeting your fears, and easing your aches, and loving yourself. Relating with others from this empowered sense of self only enhances the potential for beauty to unfold in any outside relationship."

I lowered my gaze to the hopper eyeing me. Suddenly, I some-how knew it was the same hopper that shot past my foot before I got stuck in Mud Lake. What did this little fellow want with me? Why wouldn't it move? I didn't want it. I shook my shirt gently, hoping it would hop away. Friend or not, I was not a bug person.

"Embrace yourself," He said. I mean He, not the hopper. Or . . . maybe it was the hopper. Anything is possible on the inner planes.

I kept wiggling my shirt, needing the thing off me.

"Stop brushing yourself away," He said. Yes, I think it was He, and not the hopper, though knowing Him, they could be one and the same.

"Brushing myself away?"

"The grasshopper is widely known for its ability to demolish masses of vegetation, and abundantly survive to preserve its spe-cies. It carries the warrior spirit. You do to yourself what you do to the grasshopper." He flopped His hand, palm up at my steadily ad-vancing longhaired army of darkness. "You'd rather have *them* at your heart."

"But grasshoppers can be destructive," I said.

He glanced outward. "Them too." He looked at me. "Remem-ber, grasshoppers help things to grow for they can pollinate."

I glanced outward. "Them too."

"But they will destroy you. The grasshopper will empower you to guard your heart and hop freely in this world. The grasshopper allows you to love without being at the mercy of your warriors."

"Do you really think I have a choice? I mean on the deepest

levels, maybe no matter how hard I try, I won't succeed in ridding my need for warriors. Isn't karma involved in who we attract?"

"The simplest meaning for karma is cause and effect, not involving the concepts of reward and punishment born from belief systems. You are hungry, you eat. You don't eat, you get hungry. Action, consequences. You steal, you could go to jail. You are kind, someone smiles. Natural consequences."

"So, the idea of good karma, bad karma, is but another spin off of moral judgments with a religious connotation."

"Yes. Perhaps an identity will play the theme of lawbreaker, imprisonment, and death by lethal injection. Bad karma? Maybe that identity needed that experience for reasons that transcend human cognition."

I said, "Then the things that happen to us are sequences in a larger story. A story that is difficult to intellectually understand."

"Yes. These sequences usually require the interplay of other identities. Once an identity acquires the experience needed, it can step out and move on to a new play with a different group. The former group will attract new players to the old play. Sometimes identities remain in an old play because they fear the unknown. Though unpleasant, there is comfort in their suffering. They choose to remain in relationships that are not required. They are finished with the whole worn story, but fear moving on."

"I am sick of my martyr-victim story," I replied. "I *must* make these warriors vanish. How do I make these warriors vanish? They are still advancing, even though each moment I want them less."

"Accept the grasshopper. Be your own warrior."

I tucked my chin to my chest and eyed the darn thing once more. I concentrated hard on taking it into me, on receiving its power to leap and bound and survive—simply and freely.

"The more you embrace your inner warrior, the more your outer warriors will fade. You must want your personal power bad enough to stop them."

"I want my personal power."

"You must choose freedom from them if you are to attain it."

"I *do* choose freedom."

"Yet, there is a part of you that still craves a Band-Aid. A Band-Aid would force down the genesis of your pain and keep you from feeling it. The sublimation of core pain causes traumatic relationships, accidents, and illness. This fate is commonplace to nearly everyone on earth. And the method is to find diversion in another."

"But what of my husband? Do I choose him over and over, living a life of pain merely to cover a Core Wound?"

"Sometimes we have relationships because we are *unresolved*. We, in our story, can live out sub-stories with chosen identities repeatedly in various realities, times, and places. These identities are conduits who facilitate events that stimulate Core Wounds and unleash core emotions. They help us actualize our mandates that we may fulfill our intent. Unresolved love, like un-required love, often involves expectations that the 'other' will heal our wounds, but it differs in that we have some notion that the 'other' created our pain. But they didn't. Whatever part the 'other' played was a part we needed them to play, yet we blame them. Until profound change is sought, our part in the play often lies unseen. Our wound must remain hidden to allow further exploration."

I thought of the many people who continually repeated the same love relationship patterns. I realized for the first time that this was not necessarily bad. The person simply was not finished exploring that particular pattern. For some reason that pleased me. We don't have to change anything unless we want change.

I glanced out at my warriors. This, I wanted to change. As I felt that conviction, the warriors seemed to freeze in their position. I was relieved! I said, a bit more relaxed, "So people who jump from relationship to relationship can search forever and never find the 'right one,' because they are not done exploring a pattern?"

He nodded. "Changing partners gives a new approach to an old problem. The problem will not be and cannot be solved until the pattern is broken. The pseudo-perfect lover we usually have in mind does not exist, for he or she would have to be a god or goddess to fulfill all our expectations. Romantic relationships are a human experience. Human. 'I'm only human' is a common term, yet we expect much more from our fantasy lovers and are ever trying to make them real. Why? Beauty permeates every cell, thought, and feeling of a human being. If you could witness the activities within your body alone, you would sink to your knees in awe and kiss every part of your flesh. The mind, heart, and spirit radiate this same splendor. So, who are you to berate yourself? Or anyone else? Or anything else? You can grouse if you choose. See where it gets you. Oh, places like Mud Lake, the Cave of Wounds, or well—here, in The Mine Field."

"What is a soul mate then?"

"The term soul mate is generally thought of as two bodies that share one soul. Two people who are half of each other. Yet, just as two people may bond, so can a group. That group can have an urge to bond with another group, like two molecules uniting. The molecules could keep uniting, and set into motion the awareness that all life is one entity, one soul. So, your soul mate is actually yourself in its awareness of wholeness."

"I see," I said, "because everyone is really us anyway. But the others we 'dance' with, well, how do we know when it is time for the undoing of a pattern?"

"When the unexpected comes calling, such as the revelation of a shocking secret, we are forced to stop and think. We are forced to examine our life and the meaning *of* life. Everything is quiet, and yet loud with new awareness. What had seemed to be was not. What the mirror reflected is not what is. We seem to be who we seem to be, but then in the moment of awakening, we are not. Our beliefs go blank for a moment. In that blink, we are on the other side of life where the rudder that *steers a life* is formed. In this awareness, the status-quo is unimportant. What the majority accepts becomes unacceptable. And then you know it is time to end a particular dance with another. You know it deep and you know it sure. You move on, and you don't look back."

I empathically sensed the reality beyond His words. I felt entranced, imbued with pleasant sizzling energy.

The purity in His eyes melted me. He said, "However, some cannot live without their lifelong theme, such as 'I am a victim.' They fear change. So they shake off their new awareness, and continue the old story, and keep the dance going. This choice is important for them at the time, as it has long been for me to continue my old pattern. But now, my rudder has vanished." His voice cracked. "I search the inner library for what might enable me to conclude this old story." He inhaled a quivering breath. "For me, the answer lies is simplicity, not saintliness. Gentleness, not aggression." His eyes closed. "A single moment offers wisdom like a drop of rain splashing upon my nose. The highest mountain peak does not possess more. I needn't continue with outer world achievements to experience the magic of a moment. The simplest acts of life embrace the mystery of everything. Colors change each second, ever building a fresh stage for a new experience."

In that moment, I appreciated the small things in life.

His head turned slightly. The setting sun silhouetted His profile. Behind Him, the warriors remained frozen, but I wished they would disappear. He looked beautiful as I watched His lips move. "Then each moment, face the sun for the first time, and accept that the bottomless pot of wisdom has much room yet to be explored, even if you have finished your desired achievements. The 'what if' is to experience concepts and then let loose of each concept as it is experienced, instead of claiming, 'This or that is the truth.' When the boundary of knowing is dissolved, boundless beauty awaits."

I'd been so involved in what He was saying, I forgot about the grasshopper, and kind of liked it there. I guess it didn't have to go. But, I glanced outward, the warriors who keep me from my *own* power—must.

I rose, far too agitated to sit any longer. "How did I even get here? I was thinking high-minded things when I fell with a thud."

"You were thinking about how badly you wanted warriors." He spread His hand in a theatrical arc at my army. "You got them. If you can resist them, you will have traversed the minefield, and you will enter your Core Wound. There, you can heal yourself by retracting the first stone thrown that created all the ripples of your life-long drama. Then you can begin a new adventure in the life of Susan. You have worked hard toward this end."

I was relieved that He'd noticed.

He smiled. "Susan." The way He said my named chilled me.

I returned a faint smile.

Then I realized the impact of what He was saying. There was

no need to continue quibbling about unmet needs, no need to continue blaming or avenging. We bump and smash into each other without the vaguest clue that we all created this reality as a great play to experience. We are not the players. We play at being the players. We are wholeness, in perfect beauty—always.

I wanted to feel that again, that beauty, that wholeness. My caged heart was growing wings. I wondered where my heart would fly when once I set it free. Free from having to belong to anyone. Free from fearing to belong to anyone. Because in truth, we all belong to each other. I saw my heart soaring over rivers and valleys, no longer obligated to follow social rules. My heart could move through people and things without being captured and owned. Now that was a dream to behold! The greatest dream ever.

The sun had almost set, and a brilliant moon began to rise over the horizon, shedding new light. My frozen warriors were still visible. "Why are they *still* here?"

"Because you still haven't truly released them. You have only put them 'on hold.' "

I nodded. "You are right. I suppose I have not released them completely. Deep down inside, I want protection from another. I can't seem to help that."

"Let the grasshopper of protection and freedom live—within you."

"I want to do that. I really do."

"You fear you will be found ugly, if you do that. How can you retain your heart while wielding a sword? You find it more appealing and less frightening to collude with someone else. This is not uncommon. People usually prefer to massage each other's needs—and not remember where, when, and why the needs were created in the first place."

"Perhaps you are right, but I try hard not to collude."

"Refraining is nearly impossible. Collusion creates the story."

"So even though we don't have to *collude*, we do. We *want* the adventure. Sometimes though, it seems couples work out well."

He said, "Of course. Every couple's dynamic is different. The spectrum is vast. There are no absolutes. However, the events of today have produced conditions wherein familial bonds have progressively dissipated. Tribes spread. Extended families have become rarer. To compensate for that loss, the need for coupling can be intense, the broadcasting stronger, and the rewards less. People are grabbing onto even meager rewards as a lifesaver. For most, these rewards can last months or years, but eventually most individuals become dissatisfied with their partners, and the underlying wounds flare again. In this, the bargain to meet each other's needs is broken. These unmet needs, still stemming from the deep unconscious, intensify. A new call is sounded, 'Anybody want to relate with me? I'm available.' The openness for a taker radiates in one's energy field. The call for another individual is again broadcast to enter into a new collusion, a union that again is based upon two people who *don't* want to uncover retained emotions of a hidden past."

"I guess that's also why people cheat on each other."

"In love triangles, the third person, unaware of their Core Wound, generally rationalizes why it's all right to be a third wheel in an already coupled relationship. The cheated-on usually vilify the infidel and the infidel's lover, feeling victimized. The cheater often rationalizes that the affair happened because needs weren't met. Nobody sees the whole picture. The issues will never get resolved until one journey's within to see that *all* the players unconsciously set up the situation. For instance: do the cheated-on believe deep within that sooner or later they will be betrayed? Why do the cheated-on unconsciously choose partners who would do such a thing? Even if that 'why' is elusive, knowing that we all create 'the dance' is helpful in releasing blame."

"But how do you resist attractions when they are so intense?"

"Attractions are designed to resolve subconscious issues. For you, you needed to stand up for yourself, so you attract those who would make you do that. To survive them, you need to shout, 'No!'"

"So adhering to intense attractions enables us to work through issues within ourselves."

"It can, up to the point, until its time to actually resolve those issues. These subconscious issues are unrecognized thoughts, feelings, and beliefs from many life experiences in various times and places. They are stored in vaults. When we open these vaults, and free what is in them, we become attracted to ourselves."

My Fool suddenly seemed a thousand years old. His skin shimmered from the full moon rising. His hair and beard turned a soft, alabaster white. He bowed His head and started to talk, but then paused. He tried three times to speak, not able to look me in the eye. Finally, His head lifted. "I am resolving the last of my earth business."

His face turned toward the sky. A fierce wind blew against His red robes. His poetic words matched the wind's intensity. "I have screamed the words for all to hear. I have ordered them, forced them, cried them, whispered them, and held them deep in my heart. Soon, I will share them no more." He looked at me. His eyes watered, glistening in moonlight. "For all the power I have wielded, I now pull back and become the watcher. For all the wisdom that has coursed through me, I endeavor to hold my tongue. I seek to give the gift, a rainbow wand, a relay stick, if you will, to the next runner of unfiltered wisdom. A song it is, like those passed down from ancient generations as beacons of light for the children of tomorrow. When I have passed the torch, I can then disappear. Can you hear me, Susan?" His voice cracked. "Can you hear?"

I listened hard.

He said, "Needs motive the story. If you want a certain story to end, then embrace in yourself what you want and need in others. If you do not, meeting your needs will depend upon others, a dependence that never ends. This can prove stressful if not impossible, and often the peace of it is short lived. Like weeds, our needs keep growing, and we ever look for others to tend them, handicapped to tend them ourselves. The best relationships are those involving two people who have great relationships with themselves. When two people are self-actualized, they can resonate together in harmony. Look around you. Aren't you tired of wishing for the perfect warrior *out there*? More tiring would be getting him to perform as you need, and then getting him to keep up the performance."

I glanced at the frozen warriors, my longhaired army, this illusion of what I needed. They seemed ghostly now in the descended darkness against the lunar glow. My Fool's sincerity moved me. I gazed back into the infinite depth of His eyes, appearing as two glowing orbs. He said, "My departure from the Great Earth Story nears. Use this time, Susan, to end one story and begin another. Clear the decks and receive my gift—for Highway Eleven beckons."

I choked down tears. "I *will* do my best, my very best."

His offer empowered me. Determination, faith, and a strength surged up from the center of the earth into my legs, filling my body. I surveyed the frozen warriors, all clones of a dream I'd designed to keep me from myself. To keep me from being whole because of some ancient guilt over played, over stayed, and self-made. For centuries, I'd been giving myself a fist in the face for having thrown too many punches in another reality. I had designed a theme to play out and I could un-design it. This moment. Now.

I closed my eyes and shouted to the warriors, "Be gone! I have the powers you offer. Somewhere there is a part of me that can achieve your ability." I squatted to the earth, palms summoning energy from its core. "I call my warrior power! Oh, why did I shun you! You that is I . . . you that is me! I need you back! Help me stand my ground! Where are you!"

Within my body, a whirling sensation gained speed. I gave myself to it. I zoomed inward into a vortex that seemed to have no time or space, or up and down. His words sounded in my brain as I seemed to fall away from earth. "You are determined—now. Can you hold your resolve? Will you blame your husband for your woes? Will you divorce and remarry? Will you fantasize always about the perfect love for you? Or will you become all you need? Will you own your wounds, repair them, and become what you seek?" His voice got smaller as I began to come into something. "Go to the root, Susan! Free every skeleton. Embrace your male energy. Take the grasshopper into your heart!"

I didn't know if I could succeed. I was going to a chillingly dark place to face my fears, my demons—me. I had to free myself from myself and become—more. But resisting the urge to invite a hero to save me was a monumental task.

His whispery voice split my thoughts, "Invite the hero. The hero is *you*." I saw a vision of Him, eyes pulsating challenge. His face took on a warrior glow.

I gulped. His persona was volcanic.

He tossed a gem at me. However, the whirling tornado sucked it up so quickly, I didn't even know if I received it, or saw the color accurately. But something slammed my chest like the grasshopper had. I think it was green. I think it was the Gem of Love, hard to catch, hard to hold, hard to even see it for what it was. And yet love held the cycle of all green things in their seasons, and held the promise of bearing fruit and producing new seeds. Perhaps when I knew true love, not un-required, or unresolved, but unconditional, the gem would appear in a way I could grasp it.

In my vision, My Fool bowed and continued to bow walking backwards until He faded into darkness.

I wasn't taking this journey to please Him, although it did. I wasn't taking this journey to receive His gift, although I believed I would. I was taking this journey to free myself from a static repeat that had simply worn me out. It was survival. That's all.

Suddenly a magnanimous force grabbed me, propelling me through layers of energy. I thought my skin would blow off and disintegrate my body. I couldn't inhale. Then I couldn't even think. I felt something, the green gem I think, cut my skin and blast into my heart producing immense pain.

Then, everything stopped. Dead silence. All—still.

I was in a place of beginnings. This is where I'd lost my warrior. And this is where I would find him.

If you are feeling lonely and desperate for a relationship no matter what the cost, take a beat. If you have lost something that you are searching for in others, take a beat. If you are in a destructive relationship that you cannot dissolve, take a beat. What do you need? Attention? Affection? Self-respect? Significance? Until you give these things to yourself, unabashedly and completely, whether you realize it or not, you are in the Mine Field of Love. Lay your hands over your face and feel the fear beneath. Trek into that fear with nothing but yourself, naked and alone to find your inner beauty. Then, and only then, can the romance dance be an expression of true love.

Reclaim—yourself. It is time.

Tunnel of Demons
"Begin at the end, end at the beginning."

GEM #8 CONFRONTATION

Darkness. Blinding, deafening, numbing darkness. No stimulation. Nothing. Yet, my lifeblood pumped furiously. Each breath seemed my first . . . and last. My skin tingled with awareness.

One hour. Two. Three. Still dark. Still nothing. Yet . . . everything.

Unable to stand the quiet, I sang for a long long time. Unable to stand the stillness, I stretched . . . for a long long time. Unable to stand any more, I sat on my knees and hunched over, wondering what I was supposed to do. I'd waited so long that the edge of fright had worn off. I started to get bored and sleepy.

"So, you finally had the guts to show up."

I jolted, heart pounding. A man's voice. He was in front of me, but I feared to look. I stiffened with an ancient terror that I could not explain. Finally, I forced myself to lift my head. A red glow highlighted an enraged face with explosive eyes.

Devil incarnate, I kept saying to myself.

His lips stretched back over sharp white teeth. "You made me."

He seemed a human monster, his face lined with long . . . black . . . hair.

I swallowed. "Are you the part of me I shunned?"

A fist came at my face, making contact. I fell on my back and blacked out. When I opened my eyes, he was standing over me. I felt like I'd been hit with a brick.

A wave of nausea rolled up my stomach. My sinuses swelled with tears, exacerbating the pain in my jaw where he had hit me. "You're not very nice . . . are you?

"You think *you* are nice?"

"Usually," I said, trying to sit up. But I felt too ill and went back down.

He started pacing. "You are not so nice. You ousted me, all that I am, and all that I represent," he looked over his shoulder and raised one brow, "because of that little accident we had."

I sat up, feeling so sick, pretending like my face wasn't throbbing. "What little accident?"

"The little matter of . . . destroying a world."

He came to me and knelt. His fiery gaze burned into my eyes, locking us together. Memories flooded my mind, but surely I was making them up. Then I remembered My Fool had said that the details are unimportant, that the energy or set up of an experience will reveal the key. So, I arrested my doubts. Imagined or not, skewed or not, these visions had merit.

His hypnotic dark eyes pulled me into him. This black-haired man and I were one being. Through one pair of eyes, we watched ground burning, life wilting, and millions of people writhing and screaming in agony.

I covered my face. "S . . . t . . . o . . . p!"

"Coward," he hissed, standing.

He pushed his black boot against my chest and shoved. I fell back, flat on the ground. "Isn't that what you want? To be tortured. You want me to torture you?" He stepped on my stomach, squashing my guts. "What about the way you tortured me!"

My knees curled up. I tried to roll sideways, but couldn't with his boot pinning me down. With faint breath, I eked, "How did I torture you?"

He lifted his boot from my stomach, squatted, and wrapped his hand around my neck squeezing harder as he talked. "You reached inside our being and hurled me into oblivion. I should snap your pretty little neck for such betrayal!" He paused a moment, as if attempting to regain self-control. He pushed his hand up roughly under my chin and released my neck. "But I need my gentleness, even though I despise it—you." He rose and started pacing again. His agitation mounted. "I can do nothing but destroy.

I am all that you are not. Life after life, I am motivated by lust to seduce, torture, and kill! I cannot stop it."

I suddenly realized why all my memories of other times and places involved me being victimized. The other side of me was out doing the opposite. I pushed myself to a sitting position, starting to feel sorry for him.

He came my way, stiff and mean. I feared he'd kick me. But he stopped and looked down at my trembling body. "And you think you are so innocent. How noble was it of you to leave me in this state? You blamed me because you are too weak to accept our act. You can't bear the guilt, so you want to suffer." He leaned over, grabbed my jaw and squeezed hard. "I can make you suffer." He squeezed harder. "It's what I do."

"Please." A tear streaked down my cheek, catching on his finger.

"A tear," he said, "what I would give for a tear." He released my jaw and stood straight. "Why don't you cry for *me?*"

"I'm sorry." I felt the child in me curl in shame. "Please forgive me. Please."

He squatted suddenly, pushing his face close to mine. "Please! You ask *me* please. I have pleaded with you for softness, begged for your return, craved light, and lived in endless rage because you won't acknowledge my existence. You turn your nose up at me, swearing I could never be you!"

My face ached with tears. "But you're so violent. I just can't believe it. You just *can't* be me."

He grabbed my arms, and yanked me to my feet, his maniacal face inches from mine. "Sur . . . pri . . . se." His face transposed into My Nun for a moment, then back to the warrior.

My jaw dropped.

"That's right. Your Nun is me, inverted. She is the power to attack yourself. Extrovert that power, and you see me, the power to attack others."

I tried to step back, frightened of the truth more than being beaten.

He shoved me hard, making me fall again. This up and down stuff was making me sicker. His words were worse. "You sought every man of war you could get your hands on to fight *for* you. Yet, you would not receive me and fight for yourself." He spit on me. "You are pathetic!"

I wiped the spit off my cheek.

"I despise meekness," he said. "I despise you. And that is why I destroy all like you who cross my path!"

I swallowed hard shaking my head, trying to grasp the harsh reality of my situation. The dark side of me was violent! And I—I could literally not kill a fly.

He squatted, and glared at me. And his eyes were scary. "Each time the abuser abuses, he is beating up something inside himself —innocence. He does to others what was done to him. He takes from others what was taken from him. And this gives him a false sense of power. Therefore, he can never get enough. No matter how much he feeds off others, he grows emptier and emptier, ever trying to make his victims a reflection of his own wrecked heart." He rolled his eyes derisively. "You, on the other hand, recognize worth in what you call goodness—by definition of a nun, and nothing but distaste for anything beyond your lily- white conception of what life should be."

"I have compassion for all!"

"All but yourself," he said. "Deaf and dumb the dragon is to its victim's plea."

I finished his sentence as if we were one. Well, I guess we were. "Aye, I am the victim. And aye, the dragon's me."

I realized then how I beat myself up anytime I ventured off my pedestal of what I thought it meant to be good.

His lip sneered. "Those who invite pain are weaklings and deserve what they get!"

I huffed, "Those who inflict pain are bullies and need compassion to soften their hate!"

He stared hard at me for intense moments. "Then, give it to me."

I knew I had to forgive his brutality. I knew I had to accept him as me. Nevertheless, I was petrified. "If I accept you as me, what if I become a mean person?"

"If I let you accept me, what if I become a weakling?"

"I'm afraid to do it."

He rose. "I didn't think you would."

"I want to."

He looked askance at me with narrowed eyes. "Then forgive what we did . . . and let us be one. Aren't we both done with the way things have been—with the way things are? Haven't we both experienced enough of our respective themes?"

I nodded. This had to be done. I had to do this. Ironic, that I had always wanted a warrior to save me, but in truth, I had to save the warrior *before* he could save me. I surrendered to the notion. Before I could blink, I appeared in a scene foreign to my consciousness, in a place not earth, in a time unknown. Viewed through earth eyes, the scene seemed like a rendition of *Star Wars*, hard to believe, and somewhat ridiculous. But My Fool always said, "The experience alone, whatever it is—has merit." I was not on drugs, but the experience was as real as my children. Who is it that decides what reality is anyway?

The words that came forth in this scene were not English, yet I seemed to get the meaning in a kind of subconscious translation. And though I was another character, I did not slip away from the consciousness of Susan.

I was the Imperial General of an Empress who governed our world. I was a male, kneeling to the ground, touching a substance that had saturated the soil. My long, black hair was caked with an oily residue. My clothes were black, right down to my boots.

Purple skies darkened with impending doom. I ran into the citadel, searching for my Empress. I found her pacing crystal floors in a turquoise room.

I shouted, "Empress! We must counter-attack, or we'll be destroyed." I had been advising her to counter-attack for some time, but she would not.

She walked up to me and gripped my arms. "No. We must continue using psychic means and heart energy to disarm them. We can attain a peaceable alliance, given our divine power."

I said, "We have waited too long already. We have been unsuccessful. I beg you Empress, counter-attack now!"

"No," she insisted. "We have much to offer. Our knowledge of humane warfare . . . our methods for peace, are exemplary. Once they understand our gifts, they *will* retreat."

"There is no time!" I cried.

She wouldn't listen to me, so I ordered a full-scale attack in an act of subterfuge. Within a week, our world was in ruins. I'd underestimated the enemy's destructive capability. The air reeked of thick toxic gas that had been set afire.

My people were dying. My Empress was dying. She lay half-burned on ashen earth outside the citadel. Blood coated her gold colored hair, fanning the goop on the ground. Caked ash filled the folds of her silver gown. Her sad face glistened with tears.

I knelt beside her, awaiting our impending doom.

Something was happening to her. A superimposed form covered her body, and sank into it. It was My Fool. My Fool's consciousness was now in her. I guess He had *been* her. We were in our Core Wound, re-experiencing what must be released.

The Empress struggled to speak. "I should have attacked immediately, as you suggested. They were too vicious to have been pacified. If I had listened to you in the beginning, they would have been defeated before unleashing these hideous poisons, and lighting our world on fire. My passivity cost us precious time."

My eyes stung with grimy sweat. "No. I am to blame. I was determined to attack. If I had not disobeyed your orders, we would have had a chance."

The Empress believed our world was destroyed because she'd clung to passive means. I believed it was destroyed because I insisted on aggression. Existence hung by a thread. We were forced to watch it snap. We could not breathe. Soul-shattering anguish filled the moment for us both, a moment so bleak it held all of time and space in a capsule of pain, a moment so shockingly unbearable that it forced us into the reaches of insanity.

That day, that hour, that minute, that moment, the Empress vowed to spurn passivity forever, and I vowed to spurn violence the same. She cast away heart. I cast away the sword. This set the stage for a new play in another reality. The Empress-My Fool, had played out a reign of aggressive lifetimes, despising passive means.

I-The General, had played out a reign of passive lifetimes, repulsed by violence.

But right now, in this bright new moment, we would rewrite history and change our present time.

My Fool and I talked to each other in the bodies of the General and the Empress.

My Fool in the Empress said, "All these centuries, in the perception of time, I felt betrayed by passive women, when it was I who betrayed myself. The anger I transferred to them was meant for me. Life after life, I created situations where passive women would inadvertently take me down, the very same way my passivity once brought down a world so long ago. It is not passive women I dislike. It is my own passive self, and the passive woman I once was. I had forgotten that I'd meant well, and that the sensitive heart carries much beauty. Now I can release this pain that I've stored, pain that has seeped into a thousand remembered lifetimes in a thousand ways, creating static repeat of the little drama, *Warlord Goes Down.*"

"Do you forgive yourself then?" I asked.

My Fool's voice came through the Empress, "There is nothing to forgive. This Core Event sent the arrow flying to create a Core Wound that set the stage for the bounty of experience—a grand symphony in its own right. I have been composing all along. Have not we all? I am ready to release my pattern. I have found its roots. I pull the arrow from this old heart. My conclusions change. I reclaim passivity."

My Fool in the Empress seemed to be filling with something, Her chest expanded like a balloon, and her back arched stiffly. Something in her (My Fool) was mounting toward eruption. He-she released a primal scream ripping through time and space. The cement of His-her imprisoned world exploded.

The body laying before me changed into a countless forms, a kaleidoscope of all My Fool had ever been. Then settling into the stillness of death, He seemed gone from the dead woman's body.

However, His wise old voice spoke in my mind, the mind of the General-this warrior that was me. "And what of you? What of the sword you cast away into the sea of oblivion?"

My turn.

My chest caved, clenched by unyielding claws of fate that forbade me the sword. I hunched over in a crumpled heap. I just couldn't reclaim the sword. I felt like my heart would die if I did. I couldn't bear to wield the power that put abusive people back in their place, even if it made them face their own demons and would lead to their eventual freedom. I couldn't flow the power that cracked masks and made people howl because they think their masks are them, even if in the following times they would find their true selves as never before. I could not intentionally cause pain, not for *any* reason.

"You set the stage to experience passivity, and you have. Are you not done?"

Through the General's mouth, I said, "I *am* done. I tire of the martyr-victim way. I *need* to break the cycle of my suffering."

His words flowed like music in my warrior head. "Move into the center of yourself, which is all creation. Focus on receiving the sword that is your warrior. Guilt will fade if you remove the arrow from the Core Wound. Then, you can embrace the sparkling totality of all that you are, engulfing the warrior you once were. Welcome home your warrior self, the one who lived his mandate, to fulfill an intent, so long ago, when a world was destroyed."

I felt—immense, and all the me's I ever was, were as stars in a universe that I created."

"I'm not horrible," I murmured.

"You are not horrible," My Fool said soundly. "No one is. The beginning of all things are pure, and all creation comes from a constant beginning. The idea of *bad* is but a created perception to facilitate stories that gift us with experience and satisfied curiosity."

I sighed deeply. "Then, I don't have to keep pointing a 'shame-on-you' finger at violence, and I need not be its victim. I needn't seek another to protect me. I needn't seek those who were *like* my shunned warrior self. I can have the warrior self I shunned. I *am* the warrior I shunned. 'I' can protect me."

"Yes, Susan. Time to take him back. Take back yourself."

I closed my eyes and envisioned My Warrior in the Tunnel of Confrontation. I sucked in a large quantity of air, inhaling my poor, shunned warrior self. Heat rose inside me, warm and beautiful. An ethereal fire surged through my body. Lava energy warmed all the cold abandoned places within me, melting my martyr-victim dungeon. I was breathing in freedom, freedom from being victimized, a thing I could bear no longer, not even once more. My blood raced with intoxicating adrenaline. My heart pumped long-missed joy. This reunion was everything I needed and all I had sought for as long as I could remember. Might and power melted the rage and hate I'd felt for the many who had hurt me.

I had my beloved warrior! I had my sweet temptation. I had—me. I felt my warrior crying within me. His tears held a commitment to protect me. I was . . . with me. Openings of vulnerability were sealed. For the first time in my life, I felt truly safe. Miraculously, at long last, I had no desire to convince a man to protect me. No more passive little French woman begging the strong warrior with words like, "I give you want you want, I follow?"

The scene faded. My Fool and I appeared in a familiar place. The Zone. Face to face, our bodies emitted rainbow light in crystal beauty. We stared into each other, knowing we'd both done a powerful thing.

His density had lightened—much, yet the headphones were on His head, His reminder to *hear* the music of Pure Creative Energy.

My heart felt so full. I must absorb His wisdom while I could, and learn all He had to teach, while I may.

I asked, "What we just experienced seemed like another world. How could that carry over into our earth lives?"

He said, "Close your eyes, and feel the answer."

I closed my eyes, and opened my mind. I gasped, "Hah!" My eyes flew open. "Everything exists simultaneously. However, we will experience the reality or world in which we are focused upon in *seeming* time."

His smile engulfed me. "Thus, experiencing anything and everything is possible. Carry this insight with you when you dip back into the world of identity and adventure. Remember to think polyphonically."

"Yes," I said, "Life is more rewarding when beholding *The All* while also experiencing perceived separation."

He nodded. "Open your knapsack." The headphones, snug on His ears, emitted soft music.

I pulled my pack off my shoulder, and opened the brown material, my heart racing. I saw the green gem that had gone into me as the grasshopper. In the world of my knapsack, it had fallen on a picture of my parents. I had made it through the Mine Field of Love. I *had* received the gem! I *finally* understood love.

Then, my knapsack darkened. He had dropped a large black gem to join the others.

He said, "That is the Gem of Confrontation, the exploration of unknown places, and the reclamation of forgotten beginnings. These self-created demons devour us until we confront them and make them our own. Until we own our shadow, it will own us—secretly, cleverly, seductively, and always completely."

I closed the pack. "We really do it to ourselves, don't we?"

He smiled. "We give ourselves the gift of exploration."

For the first time, I really felt the beauty of the human drama. I said, "We create such adventure! Who would have thought that the shadow that engulfs us is our own, and the light that defines us is our mind. It's like we create this rich play, and then get lost in the characters and the drama—fixated on survival, and obsessed with winning and losing."

He said, in an almost reminiscent way, "Oh, to experience the thrill of winning an argument, an award, a game, or . . . a war. Perceptions of victory elate and empower. Someone proclaims their love for us. We hold our baby for the first time. We get the job we wanted. We get the life we wanted. We have—won!"

"And what of losing?" I said.

"Perceptions of loss spotlight the tiny, separate self hurling though space all alone. 'I lost my job, my home, my lover.' Sadness, maybe anger, pervades the heart, forcing us to take stock of our lives, or perhaps we will use an experience as a springboard to create more drama. 'I lost my job, I am going to rob a bank.' 'I lost my home, I am going to drink away my sorrows.' 'I lost my lover, and for that my lover must pay!' Or perhaps we will use the loss to build something new. 'I never really liked that job. I am going to do what I have always wanted!' 'So, I lost my home. I will get a better home.' 'I lost my lover, I will work on myself.' What would life be without a sense of loss?"

I said, "I guess when you really look at it, we all win and lose, and how we react is all in our head."

He said, "As we set the scene for life experiences, we choose varieties of winning and losing, wealth and power, poverty and victimization, and countless variations in between until we are exposed to them all. Each identity milks the current focus of their life for all the experience one can have. In the big picture, there is no winning and losing for there is no separation or division in the experience of totality. In totality, all colors, thoughts, and feelings, are one energy. Judgment lives only in a world of subjective perceptions. It is not better to be powerful or powerless, thoughtful or thoughtless, passive or aggressive. Each self has power, and 'wins' in different ways."

In the blurry distance, the faraway scenes began whirling, creating a golden light. "What's going on out there?"

"Perceptions are blending, more so than the first time you visited The Zone."

The gold turned into spinning black and I could see nothing in the distance.

"Why the black?"

"Our creations come from the mystery, and blended—they go back."

Tears welled. "We haven't 'fallen from grace.' We have graced ourselves to grow and expand by experiencing individuality. We come from the void, and yet we never really leave it."

There was that smile of His again, engulfing me.

"You make me feel secure," I said.

"Nobody can give you security, only the illusion of it. If you could actually keep the security one gives you, how come the one who gives it can also crush you with a foul word, or act of betrayal? If they can take your security, was it ever really yours? Commotion creates challenge. From the ashes rises the Phoenix. If there are no ashes, how can one rise? And when the rising is done, security is *internal* and unshakably—yours."

Revelations dawned. I was able to connect the many dots of all He'd been trying to tell me. "There is no life and death, only a change of focus. We all win. We all lose. And, we never win and we never lose. No matter how the fingers of a hand relate to each other, all the fingers affect the hand. We perceive our life experience within the boundaries of our perception. Broaden the boundaries, and our life experience broadens too. Perceptions dictate our lives. Sometimes we are not done with our internal pain, so we evade a change of pattern, a broadening of perception, and a more expansive life experience."

"In addition," He said, "retaining pain causes numbness and eventual breakdown; some people call it depression. Pain's weight eventually forces us to shift focus and gain new perspective. Just as you can no longer endure the martyr-victim pattern, or I the overbearing warrior, we now end those patterns."

I chimed in, "And our pattern does not always end in death."

He chimed in, "And death is not an end, only a change of scenery. A pattern ends when we are ready for it to end. It's as they say 'all roads lead to Rome', and 'all rivers to the sea,' but the path you choose will determine what your consciousness experiences."

I squinted into the dark void. "I wonder what mystery awaits."

From my peripheral vision, I saw flickering. I looked to Him. *He* was flickering. He reminded me of drives down sunny roads on a tree filled blocks, when sunlight flickers through shadow on the pavement, almost blinding with sparkle. He looked beautiful, like heart and steel coalescing. I said, "What is happening to you?"

"My numerous selves from the *impression* of many times and places are merging, finished with their earth exploration. Old ways lack appeal, like an old skin being shed. I shine the fruits of earth exploration. Highway Eleven beckons."

"Highway Eleven." Tears glazed my eyes. I didn't want Him to leave me. I suddenly felt small—really *human*. I felt a jolting in my heart, and I almost fell from The Zone. I shifted my focus to *The All*.

He said, "The layers of myself are in full flower. Now I experience the petals of my life stories instantly and all at once, done before they were started. I have acquired the essence of my earth

Susan D. Kalior

story. I carry its fragrance with me. I no longer need the body to help me find it."

I was speechless.

He sighed sweetly. "I am done here."

"So our focus on each other, shall soon shift?"

"Soon, my dear . . . soon. I, at last have one foot on Highway Eleven. Can the other foot be far behind?"

I felt teary.

"Susan, we can never really leave each other. The One Great Self never really fractioned. It merely created that impression. All other worlds are really one world, just seemingly different. I look straight ahead, but I see my tail."

He pointed out to the darkness.

I saw that figure again, a little girl creeping toward The Zone in a golden glow.

"That is Liberty, my inner child," I said

"Yes, it is she. Do with her as I have done with you. Take the hand of one who seeks. Touch her cheek compassionately. Accept her weaknesses. Encourage her personal power, and have patience with her neophyte ways. Unconditional love. Blending your many selves will enable you to receive the rainbow wand that I hope to give to you."

"Perhaps I am ready now?"

He shook His head. "Open your hand and I will show you."

I held my open hand to him.

He raised His hand over mine and uncurled His fingers. A six inch, rainbow energy wand was there, but it seemed stuck on His palm.

I frowned. "I'm sorry."

He said, "The wand cannot fall until you not only behold the last two gems of being, but also until you utilize the one you have just received. You will be challenged to use The Warrior you have reclaimed. Until you do, all you have acquired cannot ignite in your daily life. It is as if you have built a rocket, but you still must prepare it for launch, and you still must light the fuse. When you do, and the last two gems are beheld, you will be able to receive this wand, this torch that I would like to pass onto you."

Empathy softened my eyes. I could tell He wanted to turn away and shield Himself from becoming vulnerable. But He did not. He met my gaze with equaled empathy.

At that moment, I felt Him receive me in a way He'd not yet done. His whole face opened up like a blossoming flower. Then, He vanished. I didn't know what happened to Him, but He always told me to trust life. So, I would.

The creeping girl had become clear. She reached one defined hand toward me. "Help me," she said.

Remembering My Fool's words, I took her hand. The moment of contact sent us falling like stones, hand in hand, hair waving wildly over our heads, air brushing up our faces. Down we went through a vertical hall of mirrors that reflected images: kings and queens, guru's and priests; janitors, maids, sanitation workers, construction workers, policeman, and soldiers; ballerinas, artists, singers, dancers; mothers and fathers and children and husbands and wives; old people, young people, pretty people, plain people, heavy and skinny people, smart and dumb people. Images, all of them. Images all. No substance. And I had a strange feeling they wanted it that way. Why? How could they? And yet—they did.

I held fast to the little girl's hand, squeezing it tighter as our speed picked up. Then suddenly with an abrupt thud, we crashed a structure made of playing cards, and landed on our backsides.

Can you sense your shadow self lurking deep within? This hidden self of seeming opposition, shunned from your daily life. The controlled stoic suppresses unabashed self expression. The free spirit suppresses the conformist. What do you suppress? Invite this shunned shadow self into your conscious expression. Oh, not to take over or change you that much, but rather to round out your life in a most pleasantly surprising way. It's like receiving a whole new set of skills to enrich your mundane existence. The shy become more assertive; the stoical became more expressive; the pragmatist opens to the subtle beautiful things found only between the lines. So, embrace your shadow self and then come explore with me, the Hall of Mirrors-House of Cards. See you there. Bottoms up, or in this case . . . bottoms down.

Hall of Mirrors-House of Cards
"We live to pretend; we pretend to live."

GEM #9 ILLUSIONS

Playing cards flew up around us, landing haphazardly over our shoulders and laps. A few lagging cards floated down before our field of vision. Apparently, we'd demolished a card-built guest-house, servant's quarters, or some such place because across the way loomed a magnificent card-constructed palace. In fact, an empire of artistically fashioned structures made of cards surrounded us, creating some sort of palace grounds.

I looked to the small girl. To those in the outer world, she would seem nonexistent, a part of me, an aspect of myself—yet she was very real. We all have an inner child. Yet maybe in another reality, our inner children are flesh and blood, and we are the parental aspects within them. My Fool had taught me well. I was beginning to experience backwards and forward, up and down, inner and outer, and even death and life, as the same.

There we sat, my inner child and I, in the far reaches of life's deep interior. She, who had been far from my awareness, now was at last close enough, open enough, for me to view her clearly. Her little face had a button nose and smoky gray eyes that peered into me, 'what now?'

I examined her young form, about six years old. Her messy black braids lay against a dirty, white tee shirt, and blue denim overalls. Her feet were bare. Dearly, and sweetly bare. Facade had not taken her, but neglect had.

"Where are we?" she asked.

I glanced about. "I'm not sure."

There was something familiar about this place, the style, the shape of the structures were distinctively me. Even the palace gleamed in a perfect display of black and red queen cards. I guess I did put on a pretentious air in public. That way people might not be so apt to take advantage of me, an all too common occurrence.

The little girl said, "Let's call it Card Land."

"Sounds good to me." I rose. Stray cards fell off my body, joining the heap around us. I extended my hand to the girl.

She grabbed it like a kitten latching onto a nipple. I pulled her up gently.

She cocked her head and smiled at me. "I can't believe you are paying attention to me."

I smiled back. She was too adorable. Too adorable to be me. "I am sorry I have forgotten you. I get too carried away with helping others."

She cast her eyes downward. "You let me starve while you feed everyone else."

"That is changing." I knelt to her level, and realized how emaciated she was. Even her cheeks were sallow. "You are Liberty, aren't you?"

"Yes, I am Liberty," she said with an air of intelligence. "People call me Libby. You are Susan, aren't you?"

"Yes. I am Susan."

Her gray eyes glossed over. "I have been awfully lonely." She blinked back tears and lowered her small head. Then she looked up through wet lashes. Quite suddenly, she flew into my arms, pressing her little body against me. I held her tight. "You will take care of me? You will play with me? We will squash our feet in mud together?"

I cradled the back of her head and laughed a little, readying to feed her some profound answer, when it dawned on me that I would be to Liberty, what My Fool had been to me—a wise mentor.

She looked up at me grinning. "I hope we are always happy like this."

I sat back on my knees. Wisdom rolled off my tongue as if He were speaking through me. Maybe, He was. "Happiness is elusive. Happiness has been said to exist in wealth, beauty, status, power, and achievement. Cultures have their own prescription for happiness. Families too. 'Do what *we* say and you'll be happy.' Traditions tell us that ritual is the key. While rituals, traditions, and family have a valuable place, so does being true to one's self. Some religions preach that happiness can only be found in heaven because whilst on earth, we humans sin, and are punished accordingly."

Liberty scowled. "So how do we find and keep happiness?"

"Seeking happiness by means of the outer world is fleeting, because it's derived from linear accomplishment and dependent upon the approval of others. That gets old after awhile, not to mention tiring."

She fondled her braid. "Then, happiness is found within."

"Yes."

She held her hand over her grumbling stomach. "But how do we release the need for outside approval? It's hard, isn't it?"

"It gets easier with time."

"Why does outside approval mean so much to people?"

"When people get approval, they feel worthy. Job promotions mean your boss recognizes your worth. You tell yourself, 'I'm successful.' A marriage proposal means another cherishes you. You tell yourself, 'I'm loved.' Graduations mean improved status. You tell yourself, 'I'm worth more now.'"

"I do that," Liberty said, "I base my worth upon other people's opinions of me. And if the opinion is good, I am happy because I feel worthy."

"Yes, and then what? What happens when the happiness wears off because you haven't been applauded in awhile? That old familiar empty feeling creeps up on the edges of your awareness, nagging to be filled. 'That made me happy then. What would make me happy now?' Or . . . the truer thought is, 'That made me feel worthy then. What would make me feel worthy now?'"

"Yeah," she scratched her nose, "why must we achieve and act in a certain way to feel worthy? We each do our best, so other peoples' judgments mean little."

I added, "Precisely. Great value brims in the smell of a flower, a smile, a tear, or self-revealing conversation. Our worth is constant, every moment."

She threw her arms in the air. "Let's hang on to that!"

I smiled softly. So naïve she was. Good intentions are easier to have than to manifest.

Her stomach grumbled louder.

I tugged her pigtail lightly. "You're hungry!"

"I'm hungry for freedom, Susan. I want to come out of my corner and dance amongst the trees, and sing my song as loud as I please. Now *that* would make me happy."

"A better word than happiness might be 'joy.' Freedom to be your authentic self would bring you joy."

"Are joy and happiness different?"

"Most people would say, no. However, happiness has this 'get to the end of the rainbow before you can have it' kind of attitude. Joy has a connotation of being more instantaneous, in the moment. A beautiful sunset, a cat cuddling, a sweet kiss, an inner sense. These are the simplicities of joy. Achieved happiness skirts around joy, but broadened awareness and simple illumination are forever."

I rose and extended my hand to her. She took it joyfully and we began walking toward the palace. My free hand felt weird, as if an energy swirled within it and was trying to come out. I stopped walking, and held up my empty palm. The rainbow wand sure felt like it was there. I stared into my palm meditatively, watching tiny scenes playing again, but this time, the scenes portrayed resolutions. I was there in my hand, yet here in my head, nowhere and everywhere. Resolutions sliced through time and space, because I'd stepped sufficiently enough away from time and space to view the difference between the drama, and the writer of the drama. I spoke in a trance. "Joy arrives when our inner flow emanates from our core being into the world."

Liberty added, "And that flow often counters the flow created by others. If we follow their flow, we find fleeting happiness. If we follow our own, we find eternal joy."

I was stunned in the loveliest way. I dropped my hand slowly. This little girl, though an aspect of me, had grasped my meaning. I was getting through to myself.

Her head drooped. "I've not known joy. I'm bad because I get hungry. I'm bad because I have needs." A tear slid down her cheek.

I traced my finger over the wet path. How is it I had treated my flesh and blood children so wonderfully, but my own inner child like garbage? How could I give the world to my own kids, and suck the life out of the child within? I saw it then, that what my inner child needed, I had given to my birth children, for I could not give it to myself (a nun thing). I could give to others but not to me (the martyr). I shook my head, realizing the complexity of every person.

I said, "Sometimes authority figures lead us away from joy, not really understanding what is best for us. Within us all is a wise sage. Trust your sense of things, not theirs. Nobody can tell you who you are or how you ought to be. Only you can discover that."

Her eyes rolled up. "Can I truly trust myself?"

I grasped her ribcage and lifted her to my hip, holding her fondly. "Yes, you can. I am so sorry, I haven't tended you."

She stroked the side of my face. "It's okay Susan, you are here now, and that's all that matters."

My heart warmed. The harshness I'd always inflicted upon myself began to melt. I lifted my head to her. "You are significant, as you are."

As I held her little body, she nuzzled her face in my shoulder, growing wet from her tears. Her little heart beat rapidly against mine, thudding so hard. I had treated my inner child like trash. No wonder she had gotten so far away from me. No wonder it took *me* changing to find her again. Perhaps she had a body somewhere in another time-space dimension. Maybe in her reality, I was a spirit entering her dreams at night, or her so-called imaginary playmate. Somehow, I knew all these realities existed. It was like this or like that, or all of this and all of that.

I put her down gently and viewed the palace; the cards sheen glimmered in the late noon sun. I said, "We're going to explore that palace." I smiled playfully. "Race you to it."

Her eyes lit. A child at last.

Having left my shoes in the Mine Field of Love, I broke into a barefooted run.

Liberty pumped those cupid legs after me, braids flying, and elbows slicing air. She caught up. The little dickens could go fast even without shoes.

I panted breathlessly, "You still have your soul, Libby."

"I'm trying to keep it, Susan."

We reached the entrance, a double door, made of two giant cards: the King and the Queen of Swords. No surprise really. There could be no better choice to guard the entrance into one's self. I knocked. No one answered. I'd have been surprised if someone did. After all, the house was me.

"Let's enter," I said.

"But that's trespassing," replied Liberty.

I smiled, "I don't think you can trespass into yourself. Only your own facades can keep you from entering."

We opened the giant double door and entered the Great Hall, adorned with the Major Arcana tarot cards, and packed with lavish art reminiscent of the Louvre.

Liberty slipped her hand in mine.

I said, "The front room is what people view when we first invite them into our lives. As you can see, "I pointed to the Major Arcana cards. "I invite people to see the unorthodox part of me rather quickly." I scanned the art. "I reveal the most precious part of me upfront, which usually chases people away."

We walked together toward the room's center. A small tarot card fluttered down through the air in front of my feet. It was The Fool. I stopped short, releasing Liberty's hand. I crouched to pick it up, for the first time linking The Fool card with *My* Fool. In tarot, The Fool represents newness, change, adventure, originality, open mindedness, unusual perspective, freedom, and innocence. As I rose, I caught a glimpse of oversized, gray marble feet. I shifted my focus from the card to a massive statue of My Fool by the back wall, looming like a shrine. Yes, He impacted me greatly.

I walked past sculptures and paintings of angels and dragons (my counterparts) to the magnificent gray stone work of art. Liberty stayed near me like a shadow. I careened my head upward. The statue's downcast eyes, strangely real, burned into me.

The lips moved, whispering words undetectable to the human ear. "I am The Fool."

The lips turned solid again, unmovable stone. I shook my head, *nah, those lips didn't really move.* Even in the inner world, one's imagination can get wild. I started to look at Liberty.

"To become The Fool—"

I took a double take back to His lips. They *were* moving. "—I have released the need to conquer and control others. They may appear before me," I could swear the statue smiled, "as you seem to do, but I will not go to them. That means I release you, as I know you to be. I'll no longer approach you in the Desert of Loneliness, Mine Field of Love, or anywhere else you have left to go. If you come to me, that's different. If you come to The Fool, toward newness, toward change, that's your decision."

Liberty tugged at me. "Let's go, Susan, let's explore."

I guess Liberty couldn't hear Him, but I wasn't done talking. "You go explore. I will join you in a moment."

Liberty went off exploring as kids do, seeing and touching in that aura of wonder children tend to possess.

"Tell me more of The Fool."

"The Fool," He said with moving lips and a sad sort of laugh, "The Fool views individuals as a collective. The Fool sees particles as the whole. The Fool opens the heart. I have opened my heart, and surrendered my desire to lead others. Now, I must endure a period of isolation. Physical eyes see division. Inner eyes see connection. The outer ear hears what is spoken: commands, bantering, and intellectual opinions that swirl like swarms of bees. The inner ear hears what the voice *isn't* saying: the whispering of wisdom, the silent screaming agony of those repressed, and the joyous song of those freed. The sound of music entertains. Many hear it from the outside in. Hearing music from the inside out transports one to the center of creation."

"You mean, away from what is created?"

"I mean to *before* creation created."

The abstraction dizzied me a bit.

On He spoke, "I used to trick myself, clinging to the *image* of foolhood, only playing the part. Shock them. Control them. Conquer them. I excelled at winning. I could use 'the fool' as a mere facade to continue playing the same old game. Now in my isolation,

I am connected. I grow into age rather than growing old and pining for youth. This is the way of The Fool. Great magic resides in age that can give entry to Highway Eleven."

As He spoke, I realized His commitment to remain in The Zone, or really—to go beyond it to Highway Eleven. I understood at last that The Fool was about purity without judgment, change without fear, and vision beyond boundaries.

It was odd that I had never viewed My Fool humanly old, but He was elderly, just as Liberty was a child.

"What is age?" He said, reading my thoughts, as always.

I settled in, sitting on His huge feet, leaning against His marble calf.

Beautiful words slipped from His essence into mine. "Age is a fallen leaf. A fallen leaf does not take up much room but has much to do with the future of a story. Its nutrients turn back into productive foundations for new seeds to grow. Then, I am a fallen leaf. My experiences soak into the ground around me, to promote growth for others into the future, with roots that reach into the past. This stage, or age of life bears great importance. Older people, like fallen leaves, provide younger people with an enriched foundation for new experiences yet to be discovered. It is the aged who give the nutrients that make experiences grow."

The statue started to glow, and a superimposition of leaves seemed to sprout from it, like some sort of nature god. Some leaves fell, and though I knew the floor was marble, I saw a superimposition of soft churned earth.

His tone grew more gentle. "In the dissolving leaf's nutrients, small seeds grow. These seeds carry the vibratory experience of the nutrients that fed them. The baby is of all preceding parents."

For a moment, I felt a span of generations, each giving way to the youth that followed, the youth that would carry the genetics of the old.

"I am a fallen leaf," He said. "I now lay a foundation for future generations, as did past generations for me. It is the cycle of life. The nutrients of the leaf grow a seed that turns into a tree. Is that not a great lot? The twig that once harbored a leaf could not be, if a leaf had not provided a foundation for the seed to become. Is that not a great deal? The younger grow by knowing the older. The older in their fading focus, await new growth. The decaying leaf is not the end, but a beginning in another reality."

I could see it more clearly then how, in this cycles, death and life were one. There was no end, nor beginning, not really; it only seemed so.

His voice turned almost rhythmic, "I have gazed out my great window and seen the winds of a story that has yet to find its awareness. Life's bounty unfolds its mystery to everyone always, even the elderly. The stories lived by the old, carry a vibration that lingers at the gate of their transformation, all dressed up, awaiting the arrival of the younger to come along and try that vibration on for size. Even as the elderly defocus from one world and emerge in another, they leave behind a legacy."

For the first time ever, I welcomed age.

He spoke on, almost proudly. "There is great honor in being amongst the older generations, though this honor is often experienced as small, maybe barely visible, maybe quiet, maybe totally unnoticed. This job of the aged appears little but is really so big. 'Tis the planter of small seeds, whether they take root or not. Some seeds the winds blow far far away before the conditions are right for growth. Then, patience. Send your memories off to school to be available for the students of tomorrow looking for a mission that once was yours. This is how stories are birthed. It has always been that way and will always be that way. Newness comes from oldness. Some understand that. Most do not, for youth feels itself strong and head of the class. But what would the seed be without the nutrients of a fallen leaf? I am a fallen leaf. I nurture the seeds that burrow into the foundation that will raise a tomorrow."

I wrapped my arms around His marble calves, overwhelmed with respect.

His symphonic words flowed through my brain.

"This seeming age of my body allows me to detach from life's play, and yet connect to life's source. Age is a bridge to the other side of me—and for some, the Other Side of God. Few can touch me now. Few can see me. Few can dance and play with me in the interior realm of being. Soon, I will be so deep, the true Fool, no one will find me as an individual, for my focus will have shifted to total-ity. I will be found in everything and everyone, for I will be no thing, and no one. Ah, such is the life of a fool."

I stepped back from Him, still not sure if my imagination was playing tricks on me.

The statue of My Fool said, "Now, take the child and explore your house. Explore your house of cards. I'll not follow or drop in unexpectedly. Off you go."

I gazed at Him one last long moment.

Liberty had found her way back to me, pulling my hand. "Come Susan, let's explore. Let's go into the kitchen."

I turned away from Him with conflicting emotions. I had to find the rest of myself, all the selves within me, and bring them to-gether. Yet, I didn't want to leave Him. However, I knew I must.

We walked across the Great Hall toward a smaller room. We entered a tiny, gray kitchen. Though small, it was graced with an enormously long table covered with a pink, blue, and gray table-cloth. Baskets of fruit and fresh baked braided bread surrounded fat, pink lit candles on gray marble holders.

"See Libby, this room is tiny, because I often forgot to feed myself. See, it is gray, because there is no color in my effort to tend the physical me. If I tried, guilt would set in. The Nun would arrive. Enjoying food was a sin. Filling myself was a sin. Adding vibrancy to my body was a sin. See, the table is long and stocked with food because I tend to feed others graciously. In fact, if I feed others, I think I have eaten and wonder why I'm hungry."

"It all looks delicious," she said, licking tongue over lips.

"Have some food, Libby."

She grabbed a big plum. "Have some yourself," she said.

I winced a little. The Nun, of course. But she was weak in me now, somewhat faded by my inner illumination.

Liberty said, "When you don't feed yourself, it hurts me. When you starve yourself, you starve me. Do you see, Susan? Do you see?" She bit into the plum, eating ravenously.

I half laughed, a serious, sad sort of laugh for she had spoken the truth. If she and I were connected, then all I did to me, I did to her, and vice versa. My self-deprecating behavior had been part of my outer persona. I wanted to please others. I took pride in not pleasing myself. The true martyr. Those days must end. I grabbed a large, red apple and bit deep. Juices squirted out, and landed on the corners of my mouth. Bully for me!

I chewed, enjoying the flavor.

Liberty swallowed the last of her plum and spit the seed into her hand. "We're feeding ourselves, and that is good. We will need to be well nourished and strong to sing our song to the world."

I thought about what she said, 'Singing our song to the world.' I knew that beneath the conscious play, all are enlightened already, yet I could see the role I had designed for myself. The role was an educator for those who sought depth. Oh, not of preaching this or that, but one of many, pointing the way inward to embrace one's significance in the dancing fires of creation.

Liberty put the plum pit in her pocket. "I will plant it later. It must have a chance to grow."

"I like how you think, Libby."

She eyed the bread. "May I have more?"

I nodded, "In fact, let's sit."

We pulled out the wood chairs and feasted. I finished my apple and consumed half a loaf of steaming brown, chewy bread. Libby ate a whole loaf. Had I starved her that much?

From somewhere deep inside me, I heard My Warrior's voice. "Meat, I want meat."

I replied, "Not now, not yet." He needed me to feed him, to use him. He was in my house already, in me, accepted by me. Was that not enough?

Liberty grabbed a handful of plums and stuffed them in the pockets of her overalls.

"That's the spirit!" I said.

Libby sprung up. "Let's explore some more!"

Such a child, I thought, *such a wonderful, beautiful child.* How is it I neglected her for so long?

She raced ahead of me. I followed her into the laundry room. At least there was no dirty laundry. I had been washing it since I entered the inner world. At last, I'd begun to deal with unfinished business and shameful memories.

I followed her downstairs and explored the bedrooms. Each bedroom held an aspect of my personality. Some aspects were facades, like the business woman, the shy little girl, and nun. Some aspects were hidden parts of me that sought expression, like the passionate poet, and burgeoning woman. Every bathroom was clean, but untidy with clothes and toiletries. My effort to care for the world had afforded me no time to keep order within myself.

Those rooms caught my attention, but the real shocker was the rumbling beneath us. What, oh what, was in the basement? We descended to the level through secret doors that led to dark stairways and mazes like the catacombs of Rome.

One room held a pacing tiger, the place I put my anger so no one else would see it. I knew I must free the tiger from its cage, and use my anger to create positive action. And I might need My Warrior for that. Another room was a tomb where the sleeping priestess lay. And yet another room led to an ocean that harbored a wise whale whose wisdoms wanted to surface, and a dragon who could give it passage—if I so allowed.

However, the room that scared me most, was the one where I had put The Warrior I'd reclaimed, but not channeled through me in my everyday life. He was locked inside, in fact so locked in, I didn't actually enter. I just knew he was in there. I did have him. I did. I just feared using him.

One by one, I freed the others, but not him. I couldn't. Not yet.

The tiger dashed up the stairs. The dragon hissed fire, burning a passage to the top part of the house. The whale surfaced. The priestess floated upward speaking in ancient Egyptian tongue.

Suddenly, an avalanche! The house of cards crashed fast and hard around me and Liberty. I grabbed Liberty protectively and crouched. Thousands of cards fell on top of us: walls, the roof, pieces of bedroom. Paintings smashed. Food splattered. We were buried in a paper mountain. I pawed the cards away from our heads until we could both see. A structure zoomed down from above, smacking the ground with a thud, landing in front of us. The statue. The statue of My Fool!

I shook a card off my head and examined Him for damage. He looked unharmed, a miracle.

I asked, "What are you doing here?"

I heard His words like whispers in my head. "You've made me a hypocrite. I told you I'd not drop in on you anymore, yet here I am. I hardly had a choice, but since I'm here." His eyes widened, "Congratulations. You crashed your persona."

The house of cards crashing was an inner world thing. The reflection of that occurrence in the outer world was worse. All hell broke loose. My husband and I were drifting far apart because I embraced myself so brightly, our unwritten contract of *I give you want you want, I follow*, had been broken. I started nurturing myself more, and expending less energy on others, because my tiger, priestess, dragon, and whale needed to be free. Chaos was everywhere.

We continued our telepathic conversation. I said, "I crashed my life."

The statue of My Fool said, "Rainbows follow storm. One day your whole body will glow like a rainbow."

"Yeah, yeah," I replied sarcastically. "Well I'd better go see if I can make sense of this mess."

The statue of Him said, "The mess is as it should be. Now you can rebuild, but you must enlist The Warrior."

"I can't. Not yet."

"Prolong the chaos if you must." And though He was a statue, I could swear He shrugged His shoulders.

Then the statue seemed just a statue. The spirit of Him was gone, and that upset me. I didn't know where He went, but I was sure we would meet again—well . . . I hoped. Yes, I had yet to use My Warrior, but at least I hadn't beat up my inner child. At least I didn't blame Liberty. She appreciated that, I could tell.

I felt something solid in my hand. I opened my palm and stared at it. I hoped it was the rainbow wand, but it was a brown stone, almost like any other. Brown for the ordinary, for the overlooked, for the illusion of real. And yet, of all the stones He'd given me, this seemed the most precious. When I realized that, the brown turned to a brilliant citrine orange that reminded me of the sun. Wisdom flowed from the gem, as if it could speak. Yes, the gem was talking to me. "We pretend to live, we live to pretend. Only when the house falls, do we realize we were never alive at all. Only when everything crumbles, and burns away, do we realize there is more to existence. Only then, do we awaken, recharge, and recreate. Through hell, we find heaven."

Oh, where was my heaven? A tear dropped from my eye and splashed on the stone. I held onto it, not ready to let that wisdom settle into my knapsack.

I sighed hard, and nodded to Libby, a 'let's go' gesture. "Let's find heaven," I said.

"Let's do," she replied.

We climbed the heap of cards. When we arrived at the surface, the whole kingdom looked like a war zone. Where was the rainbow? I couldn't find it. The sun was setting, and I was exhausted. "Let's sleep Libby, but not in this wreckage."

"Whatever you say, Susan."

We walked away from the broken land and curled upon solid ground, but sleep didn't come easy for me. I wasn't finished going through hell. The storm wasn't over, not by a long shot. Would I survive? I did not know.

It feels that way, like hell, like death, when you face yourself and shed old ways—when you let the world crash around you so that you can finally, finally be free. Everyone has amazing potential. *You* have amazing potential. Will you emerge from your shelter and let yourself grow? Many of you will turn and run from this point of breaking, and race back across the State Line forgetting the inner realms. Stay safe, don't rock the boat, suffer in silence. Many of you will not have the courage to go further, not ready to change your life and allow your life to change. Metamorphosis—caterpillar into butterfly. But if you *are* ready, if you choose to fly, if you do . . . be courageous, oh seeker, and READ ON.

Surviving the Quakes
"Destruction Births, and Birth Destroys"

GEM #10 TRANSITIONS

Liberty and I slept not far from the rubble of cards that night, but we woke up on a filthy sidewalk in a slum reeking with frenzied energy. Something wet had soaked through my very holey, ragged shirt. I sat up. Oil. Yuck. My feet were still bare, but grimy as grimy could be.

Liberty sat up beside me. "Where are we?"

We glanced about with cautious eyes. The shock on our faces aborted words.

Teenage gangsters eyed us curiously, baggy blue jeans and baseball hats worn backwards. Savage sparks in deadpan eyes revealed a story of desperation, of a conscience not being heard, of humanity curling in a ball to die: these teenagers, these gun-toting children lost to the night.

An unkempt man in ragged blue jeans spit out a wad of chew and began walking toward us. His red, balding hair stuck out all over the place. His dirty face matched the naughty expression in his eyes. The teenagers watched.

I inhaled deeply, coming to only one conclusion: Liberty and I needed to get out of here! Oh, where was My Fool? I glanced about for a path of escape, when I glimpsed—Him, My Fool, so faint, glowing in a rosy light. He was leaning against a graffiti-covered brick wall with Sony Walkman headphones on His ears, casually enjoying His music, seemingly oblivious to the slum-like environment. Perhaps by needing Him, I found Him. Oh, no matter. He was here!

It was nice to see Him 'de-statued.' He seemed invisible to the crowd.

"Liberty?"

"Yes?"

I pointed to Him. "Do you see that spirit-like man over there with earphones on His head, leaning against the brick wall?"

Liberty nodded. "Yes, I do."

"He is known as The Fool. He is invisible to many," I said.

Liberty snuggled closer. "*We* aren't invisible though."

"Come on Liberty." Since He would no longer come to me, I grabbed Liberty's hand and sprung up so fast, I couldn't remember doing it. We walked briskly toward My Fool.

Our feet smacked gunk on the street. I tried to appear casual, but fear held me stiff and weighted my lungs. Predators can smell fear. The weight of street-eye stares crushed me with a sense of impending doom. I considered using My Warrior self, but I wasn't ready. I just wasn't. I had made peace with him, and I was willing to use him one day—and that was enough for me—for now. I wasn't quite ready to be confrontational, or hurt people's feelings even if they were hurting mine. In his world, My Warrior was probably trying to summon me, trying to make his gentleness and compassion emerge, but it just wouldn't. Oh well, there is always tomorrow.

We arrived in front of My Fool. He squatted to Liberty. "Welcome, child."

I glanced about the streets, watching the watchers.

Liberty said politely, "My name is Liberty. I seek freedom."

"I am visible to such seekers," My Fool said, "for I am in transition to Highway Eleven."

Remembering that, I forgot my fear for a moment. I gulped. "Can we come?"

My Fool's words felt like a drill through my gut. "You must find your own way."

Liberty asked, "Where are we?"

My Fool answered, "In Susan's world."

It made sense when I thought about it, that the atmosphere of my inner world would appear this way currently, for my outer world was falling apart. I was separated from my husband who had replaced me with another. My children were going through harsh adjustments, and I was nervous about making it on my own. I had witnessed a car accident where a little girl died, and a few of my cats were eaten by wildlife. Anxiety permeated my body, weakening my health. Anger, sadness, fear, and depression had swallowed me whole. I was fighting with all my might to blossom, even in the wreck of my transition.

Liberty asked, "Is there more than one world?"

My Fool replied, "For every world within an identity, there is a world without. Hence, there are many versions of earth reality. These related earth realities (worlds) are so close to each other that it would appear they take up the same space."

Liberty's eyes grew big, and I found her adorable in the midst of this chaos.

My Fool shifted to a sitting pose, still glowing rosy. He seemed unaffected by the dirty street as if He were sitting on an invisible cushion.

Liberty sat too, only she sat in gook. She grimaced, but held her attention on My Fool.

"These many earth worlds," He said, "are the projections of multiple versions of reality. As the sun shines its rays simultaneously, all versions of reality exist concurrently. As spokes of the wheel emanate from the hub, all spokes simultaneously spin and propel a journey. However, one's reality depends on the location (perception) of one's focus.

"Well," she asked innocently, "can we change our reality, our version of earth?"

He said, "As a person, we have free will within the margin of our intent. However, our intent for living was born of free will, so in a way we purposely restrict ourselves that we may have the intended experience. If the world that we created has gravity, we will not have the free will to ignore it. If we created our identity with a drive to dominate, we will be dominating. Yet we will have power to experiment with *how* we use our governing energy."

Even though my environment unnerved me, I decided to join them and sat on gook, next to Liberty.

My Fool continued, "Then in our daily choices, we create consciousness. There will be many others who share our location, our focus, our reality. We individually and collectively push our focus world to its limits, usually blind and unknowing of Pure Creative Energy. Then, everyone who shares that focus world is moving forward, living their intent. Some, with intents fulfilled, choose to repeat the cycle of that experiment again. Others choose to move on to another adventure. Those who move on are not more evolved, for we are all one. Those who move on are merely ending a cycle, readying to begin a new one."

Liberty asked, "Mr. Fool?"

"Yes, little one," He chuckled.

"Do worlds ever die?"

He answered, "Everything always is. Only the focus changes. When a focus changes, *sometimes* the physical body appears to decay, but it simply dissolves because the energy that projected it has slipped into another reality. Death is merely a change of address. We now live and work elsewhere. Nothing dies or is ever born. It simply appears and disappears, attracted to a world that vibrates to the *same reality* that the identity *has become*."

"Wow," I said. "So, as we change, our world changes."

His head nodded in approval. "Yes. Yet, the concept of birth and death encoded in our bodies and our brains, gives our experiences meaning. If we did not accept death as an end, we would have no fear, no compulsion to live a full life before we die. Few experiences would be had. If we didn't accept birth as a start, we wouldn't have the impressions of beginnings, which bring hope and anticipation of a future. Life as we consciously know it is significant, wonderful, and necessary. We are not required to understand the complexity of Creative Energy. All beings in the entire Universe are experimenting and experiencing what has been set forth by *themselves*."

I was becoming quite involved with what He was saying and less focused on my surroundings. It was odd. I felt like we three held hands in a circle even though our hands were in our laps.

"So," I said, "when we finish experiencing a certain reality, our focus changes, not always with the dissolving of a body, and yet when a body dissolves—the focus *has* changed."

"Yes, and this is so with all identities, animal or otherwise."

Liberty spoke with an excited gasp. "What about larger groups, in countries, continents, or the whole world? Can groups change focus too?"

His rosy glow seemed stronger, and His form less visible. He said, "When it's time for a community to transform there is an increase in medical problems, mental illness, random gang violence, and crime. When the collective conscience of humankind is ready to transcend worlds, then extreme events happen: earthquakes, floods, famine, collapsing economy, terrorist acts, wars, and catastrophic accidents. These are signals that transitions are in play."

His words made my heart pound. He was right. People are so terrified to let their small worlds fade away. Yet eventually, life forces the small worlds to change. War rages, affecting thousands, maybe millions. Or an invention, such as television alters everything.

Suddenly, all the progress I'd made to change my life seemed monumental now. I already knew what it took to be real and bust free from the social mask. This *was* scary, but not as scary as it would be if I was still putting all my energy into being 'the good little girl who mustn't rock the boat.'

A pesky horsefly landed on my forehead. I brushed it away, wincing. Stupid fly. "So," I said, "if we change our state of mind, we change our reality, and thus our world?"

The fly landed on Liberty's hand. She shook it off. "Yes, Mr. Fool, "I want to know that answer too."

The fly started to come toward My Fool's rosy glowing face, but it stopped cold, and then zoomed away humorously fast. I almost laughed when He answered Liberty's question. "Yes, you live in the world that *you* perceive, even though the players in your world might perceive *their* world differently. They might live in a world viewed as synchronous, or a world where cataclysmic events are god-induced. Some view the world as evil, others as beauteous. One's view of the world is their reality. It is *their* world and *the* world. Right now the three of us are in the process of leaving behind the world we have known, which does not necessarily entail the dissolving of the body, and emerge into a new world experience, and not the same one for each of us. We are all in transition."

"Maybe that is why we have converged," I said.

Liberty shrugged her shoulders and sighed. "I want to leave behind the lonely world and enter a world of friendship."

He said, "I want to leave the world that invites me to conquer and instead, retreat into the collective."

I said, "I want to leave a world of cruelty and instead see it as beautiful."

He raised a brow. "Then you know what you must do. Remember the last time we went through the transition of a world? You wanted to fight. When we lost, you revoked that power. Though you have retrieved this power you fear, you never released it from the house of cards, Susan. You haven't released it from yourself. You are not yet using it to help forge your way. If you don't, you will become the victim again, and try as you might, it will be hard for you to view the existential meaning of chaos."

I scowled with a sigh. He was right, but still, something in me kept pushing The Warrior down. I was too afraid, even though I knew The Warrior was my savior.

"And you," I said to My Fool, "does leadership yet tempt you?"

He smiled gently. "No. Not anymore. I have at last reclaimed my passive self and nearly gained full passage to Highway Eleven. Only one task remains." He looked into me with deep knowing and I had a vision of the rainbow wand. He said, "After that, my intent will reach the sea of conclusion."

Our eyes locked for a moment as if laboring to convince ourselves that we could accomplish this last task.

Liberty blurted, "What about me? What do I need to do?"

"You little one—" He raised His rosy finger and arced it downward in the air over the line of Liberty's cheek. She tilted her head, as if her cheek had been stroked, "need to listen and learn, and stand by Susan. She needs you."

I furrowed my brows, wanting to believe I didn't need her, but rather that it was *she* who needed *me*.

He looked into me. "No. No. You'll see."

Then all at once, I felt weighted with the world's woe, its confusion and its terror. I saw beyond the phony smiles and pretend solutions that covered the heart of the problem that nobody actually understood.

I stared at the oil streak on what was left of my jeans. My jeans would never be the same and no amount of washing would get out the stain, and no amount of sewing could stitch up the rips. I had to face it, my jeans were ruined. My cover was fading. The world was ruined. The world was fading. My world, anyway. Only a new pair of jeans, only a new world, would do.

I had a sense that I'd have to be metaphorically naked for awhile, until I could tell the difference between the roles I played, and my authentic self. My heart ached less from empathy, than the realization of the part I wrote for myself to play. This part I very much feared playing, and honestly, I wasn't sure I could.

I choked down tears. "The world is going mad, isn't it?"

"*Your* world is." He said, "Sanity is regained by diving off the cliff of intellect, into the deep pools of one's quintessence. Believe once again in the guidance of the untutored soul. There is no such thing as a world out of rhythm, despite how it may seem. Balance is always maintained. If there is no oil, we will be forced to find other solutions. If grocery stores close, we will be forced to grow our own food. If the economy collapses, we will be forced to adhere to the natural world."

I winced. "That sounds horrible, yet beautiful, like lava over-flowing to create new land."

He said, "The collective conscience of earth rhythms pound like waves on the shore. Time to recede; time to move forth. Time to inhale; time to exhale. Every so often, there comes a time on earth when wisdom returns, often flowing through the mouths of people, to restore calm. Time to remember a little of what we have forgotten. That time is at hand. Mythically, it would equate with the return of Excalibur, a time of great conflict to restore Oneness with the Land. We've been progressively experiencing a growing sensation of separation. Reality to most is a television set, car, house, and three square meals a day. Smiles, and colors, and the howl of the wolf have faded in meaning."

Liberty hugged herself so hard, her little knuckles almost turned purple. "People are losing their spirit, becoming the shell instead of the substance. How horrible!"

"Not horrible," He said, "just a part of a cycle."

I rested my hand on Liberty's shoulder, hoping she'd relax.

He said to her, "To be a part of this earth cycle now is to travel a road that will yield rewarding results as we dramatically reshape our image, facade, and perception. Quantum leaps will be available to those who allow their beliefs to broaden."

Liberty's arms slipped to her sides. She seemed relieved. "So, if we choose to live in a glass jar, the jar will eventually be shattered because that is the way of life—change. But if we welcome change, then we will experience . . . freedom?"

Freedom. That was Liberty's favorite word.

He chuckled, and looked at me. "She is a wise little you, isn't she?"

I looked at her askance, but said to Him, "Literally."

He said to me, "And you are the reflection of my sensitivity."

I smiled. I liked that thought. We were each other's creations.

A bottle smacked the ground. I turned toward the noise and saw it shatter. That red-haired, grimy guy held the broken bottle up to a teenage gangster. Bums lining the sidewalk stirred. Roaming gangs gathered.

"Can we get out of here?" I asked.

"No," He said. "Escape isn't possible from anything unless you examine your belief system, image, facade, perception, and nature. Then you will have clues to why this disharmony is occurring. Would you seek the cure without knowing the cause? Would you find a temporary solution, like leave this place, but have your home burglarized? What is the cause of your disharmony, Susan? What are you afraid of?"

I gulped. "Cruelty."

"You fear the death of heart. You fear becoming heartless. You fear it so gravely that you feel the world's pain, and you will never cease fearing until you take the chance on The Warrior you have reclaimed, but not yet used in this time and place. You must act as a warrior and see if you lose heart, or not."

A high-pitched voice came through my gritted teeth, "I *don't* . . . want . . . to do . . . that."

He mimicked me. "Still . . . it must . . . be done."

I grimaced.

He said, "The pool of static repeat is teaming with those who refuse to view their belief system as a contributor to their problem. It's human nature to experiment with different beliefs. Sometimes we get so far into a belief system, we have difficulty getting out."

I rebutted defensively, "I can get out."

He said, "It takes more effort to resist change than it takes to accept it."

"I'm not resisting!"

"You are, Susan . . . you are."

I scowled.

His rosy hand moved over the top of my head, not touching. It felt good. "When you are truly done with the martyr-victim pattern, you will not just grip the sword, you will *use* the sword."

I hugged my stomach.

His hand withdrew.

"I think she *will* use the sword," Liberty said taking my hand. "I believe in her."

I smiled down on Liberty.

He said to her, "The question is, does she?"

I looked at Him skeptically. That was a problem. Did I believe in myself enough to let The Warrior move through me?

He whispered almost hauntingly, "Dissolve the question that holds your suffering in place."

My defensiveness diminished. "What question?"

"The question you ever ask, secretly, silently almost beyond your awareness is . . ." His eyes glinted, "How can I save *every-thing*?"

My heart felt daggered. I lowered my head, but raised my eyes. "You found my hiding place."

Liberty rubbed my arm. "It's all right, Susan. It's time to come out."

He said, "You will experience a new world. Just as I relinquish the concept of my identity's power, it is your turn to take it."

"And what of you," I said, "what is next for you?"

"I am attuning myself to the energy configuration of Mahler

Symphony No. 9, to attain balance for my transition into the vibration of Highway Eleven." He adjusted His headphones. Still cross-legged, He leaned back on the wall and closed His eyes. His face softened. Faint tones of music escaped from the headphones, making me want to soften too. He looked picturesque.

He said, almost melodically, "The essence of this music, to me, is synchronistic totality. Behind the mundane curtain, I can see who I am. I will move forth without reservation or restriction. I can be the ocean, the mountain, the desert, a bush, a tree. I can be the light shining through, or anything I choose. Is that not what we all seek? To again *become* for the first time. To create and know one's self once more . . . always, always, always for the first time—as we are never stagnate, but ever expanding just like the Universe, ever becoming more than we are."

I felt like He had melded us into the symphony, energy rays dancing, entwined, and making the symphony *more than it was.* I felt the essence of the music's vibration, deepening as He spoke. "We cannot stop this creative process. Loneliness drives us into it."

The ground rumbled slightly, but I had faith this moment and I rode with the music of His words. Liberty clasped my hand and squeezed. I squeezed back, assuring her.

His voice became very sing-song, yet empowered, "The illumination of Self has no boundaries, walls, location, space, or time. The meaning of life is to create, experience, discover, release, dissolve, and reemerge expanded." His voice calmed into a lullaby, "This day of days, after a night of nights exploring the center of the earth and all that holds it together, this self rests on the winds with this Mahler symphony."

The earth rumbled louder. My eyes grew wide. "Is this it? The change?"

He opened one eye. "Seems so."

"But you talked like we had a little more time!"

"No, Susan, I talked of transcending time."

Liberty squeezed my hand harder. "Death seems easier than struggling to stay alive in this changing world."

"Oh Libby," I felt sad she thought that way, even though I did too.

"Liberty." His eyes opened. He leaned over to her. "Physical death ends nothing. The human condition is a beauteous blending of experiences that fashion bountiful creations. Behold it, and your world changes while in your current physical body."

I smiled at Liberty, and kind of at myself too. "It's like opening to beauty."

Liberty said, "I just want freedom."

He rose and stood straight, shoulders back, inhaling the seeming world, and exhaling the same. He appeared refreshed. "Freedom is an important human event. But what is freedom? Freedom from what? Freedom from other people's expectations? Freedom from self-image? Freedom from oppression?"

"Yes," Liberty rose too. "That sounds good."

I stood up and joined them. "And freedom to blossom to our full potential."

"Then understand this," He said to us both. "Steel rods cage our memories, perceptions, and references to ensure a certain life experience. When we wish that experience to change, the steel rod walls will begin to dissolve, freeing us from the constructed self. Keep the essence. Release the rest. Then we are free."

He jolted as the music's sweeping beauty slipped into the air allowing me to hear the faint sweet tones. His eyes closed and He spoke like the composer He'd been in other times and places. "The music punches with lightning bolt strength, then floats with the gentleness of an ocean sunset, and lifts with the hope of the sunrise over the meadows that hug great mountains. The polyphonic music sounds a call to hear and heed the need for completion. The call pulls gently, then it shoves with force, and pleads with wisdom." His eyes quite suddenly locked into mine, hurling comet wisdom. "Be calm in the storm, Susan."

I felt the storm, behind me, threatening to engulf me. And suddenly it felt more real than anything. Panic seized me. I trembled violently. This was the day of days, the moment of moments, the moment of reckoning!

The earth rumbled louder, and began quaking. Fear flashed in my eyes.

He said, "All around you the earth may crumble, but it is your fear and clinging to what you think you need, that makes it so. In this moment, release the idea of individual identity. Experience Pure Creative Energy in its totality."

A crimson light glowed around Him. His physical body turned almost transparent. I swallowed hard with tears in my eyes. "I'm trying," I murmured. Hot liquid trailed down my cheek, landing in the corner of my mouth. I tasted the salt. I focused on the inner calm, on the oneness, on the concept that beyond our individuality, we are all the same.

The streets filled with rushing people emerging from buildings in a frenzy, insanely pushing and trampling each other. Others seemed robotic, milling around slowly, empty of heart and hope. This was my fear. This is what my fear did to me. I focused harder on the inner calm, the one great energy.

No one seemed to notice My Fool, but they noticed me and Liberty, bumping up against us. I grabbed her close to me, trying to assess what to do. I saw much suffering, feeling pulled into that current, that focus, the pain of others. Releasing fear was so hard, I think because it was tied into the idea that we were separate from each other. If we weren't separate, then there would be nothing to save, and no one's pain could be greater or lesser than our own.

Buildings collapsed. People screamed, crushed by the blows. I called for Him, "Don't leave us! The people need you. Guide us! Lead us! Help!"

He said calmly, "Your fear is doing this to you, Susan. Your reality comes from your perception."

"But we need your help!"

"You do not."

"We do!"

"All is well," He said.

Before Him there appeared an eleven-foot arced bridge of red light. Though the bridge *and* My Fool were invisible to most, a few identities walked toward Him and began crossing the ethereal bridge. His words echoed inside me, chillingly. "The distant train from Highway Eleven arrives for those ready to hang up their identities, for those whose unidentified desires have called to claim their natural right to reunite with Pure Creative Energy—to again be in the seat of that flame that burns so strong!"

I grabbed Liberty's hands and tried to cross the bridge. An unseen barrier was in place.

He cocked His head, eyes loving. "Not yet. Even I am not quite ready."

"You aren't leaving us yet?"

He shook His head almost a little fed up that I never seemed to understand that leaving is an illusion.

In an anxious voice, I rattled on, "Well, when you cross the bridge, Liberty and I want to come with you. Why not? We are all connected. Nothing is really happening. There is really no where to go or nothing to do . . . remember?"

"And yet . . . there is."

"I don't want to be a warrior!"

He raised His brows. "Yes, you do."

I almost suffocated on the lump of tears pooling in my throat. The gob moved out my eyes. I started crying. My fear turned to terror, a terror so great my world was crumbling. And it felt like the earth was being consumed with violence and suffering.

Liberty clung to my waist as a hunk of steel shot past us.

Another identity crossed the bridge and disappeared on the other side.

A store window exploded. I whimpered like a child, "Ohhh."

A brawl broke out to the side of us. Liberty didn't relinquish her hold on my waist.

He said, "These catastrophes are simply a climax in the symphony of you. You cry for help because once more you are being swallowed by a facade, the damsel in distress. You, like most, cry desperately in the deafening silence of secret agony, reaching for that stranger to pay some attention, reaching for that familiar person to give what is needed, waiting to be recognized as significant. When reaching out does not work, and there is nothing left to reach for, the cry intensifies. Behind stone faces and false smiles, are screams pleading, 'Save me!' Our inner wailing shakes the earth to wake us up from this dream called life. The walls crash around us. Our masks strip away, because in the light of such chaos we can be nothing—but real. We scream for freedom, because we can't be caged in the mirror anymore. When caged too long, we starve for Pure Creative Energy. Thus the cosmic inhale, the reuniting with our source, coming home to the flame maker, remembering just enough about our roots to sigh with relief, before setting off for a new adventure. A new adventure awaits you, Susan. First, resolve the one you are in. Release your current perceptions!"

I heard Him speak. I heard Him. Yet, terror raged within me. I cried out, "I thought had come further than this. I thought I had outgrown this."

"You are slipping back," He said, "your prerogative."

"No," I exclaimed. "I cannot slip back now, when the symphony is at its height!"

"Then do not fear the changing of your world, Susan. Let it burn and destroy your limited perceptions."

I cried, "But you are leaving soon, and I don't believe I can do any more without you."

He shook His head again in that subtlety frustrated manner. "I am someone who helped you break free from image and empower yourself. But it was you who summoned me into your life because you were ready to change. I am an aspect of you. In truth, you saved yourself, in the same way that only you can victimize yourself."

"I'm *afraid* to trust myself."

"Turn around, Susan."

"I don't want to face the chaos."

"Turn around, Susan."

I feared to turn around and face my world. What if a bottle hit my head, or a bullet my heart. An arm came round my neck and pulled me backwards. Liberty fell away from me. I tried to pull the arm off me. I saw My Fool's arm thrust toward me, and then a flash of a brown gem fly in my mouth, like a clog of dirt, yet I knew it was the arm that choked me. I couldn't breathe.

Liberty screamed.

"The Gem of Transitions," I heard My Fool say from a seeming distance.

The wisdom of the brown gem choking me was the tyranny of truth. If we don't swallow it, we choke on it. We are forced to live by being forced to die. Natural Law was like a big hospital machine that forced you to breathe. Maybe our will wasn't our own. Yet, the brown of the earth also was a foundation to grow in. There were no changing colors of this brown gem, brown was brown, rich for the growing, or the home of the dead, ashes to ashes, dust to dust.

I heard the world shouting at me. I seemed to split into a million factions sliding down into holes like worms. Ideas pushed me down, 'You don't measure up. You live in fantasy.' Slithering down. 'You are insane. Your ideas are stupid. You don't know what you are talking about.' Down. 'You aren't real.' I'm not real. Slithering down . . . mindless, heartless, nothing.

The worlds suffering infiltrated me. I'd lost my focus on *The All.* I knew only pain. *Thirty people die in an explosion. Two ten-year- olds kill toddler. Terrorist harm hundreds with noxious gas in subway. Earthquake kills thousands in Japan. Riot breaks in L.A. AIDS epidemic is sweeping the world.*

The world is I. Why do I do this to myself?

The chokehold tightened. I blacked out.

Sometimes it's okay to black out. Sometimes you have to feel immobilized, or be torn apart, or go insane. Sometimes you're just not perfect, or right, or strong enough. I didn't know it then, but on the deepest levels, there is no failure. Ever. The human struggle is noble and beautiful, and much to be admired. Oh, behold your personal struggle and pledge allegiance to your dear beautiful self. Let all else fall away. Jump into your being. Sink, down, down, down, and rise high, high, high. Melt and resurrect. There is only one truth. And that is you.

Walking the Rainbow
"To bring it all together, you must let it fall apart."

GEM# 11 SYNCHRONICITY

In my blackout, I had a dream. I walked through rainbow mists wearing a black hooded cloak. I was barefoot. His voice, warm and comforting, sounded from all directions as if through loud speakers. He told a story. But it was no ordinary story. It was to me the greatest story ever. A story of heart. My story.

His words wove through my broken soul, piecing me together.

"Once upon a time in a land far far away, there was a small girl. Oh, she was big enough in size and in wisdom, but she feared to speak her mind. She viewed life differently than most, and she didn't want to be hurt in her heart where she truly lived.

"Her mentor was a warrior of the spirit. They had many talks about life and its deeper meaning, which was different than what most thought. The majority wouldn't take responsibility for the state of the land and the actions of the people, so they pretended that what was real—wasn't, and what wasn't real—was. She knew what *real* was, but if she spoke, criticism, even harm might befall her. So she let her mentor do the talking. He received praise from few, and criticism from many.

"He always told her, *If you hide your truth, and say and do what the majority want, they will like you and they will love you. And you will be a leader of those who wear blinders, until something goes wrong. Then these people will say, 'It is not I who is responsible for humankind's ill fate. It is the fault of leaders, or a supreme being who punishes us because some speak sacrilege and nonsense of all the magic that cannot be.'*

"The girl loved to talk with her mentor and hear how life could be, if only the people had the courage to live inside their hearts. She wanted to live in her heart, but viewing her mentor decried for living in his, frightened her too much.

"One day in particular, a bold man proclaimed her mentor evil, and tried to remove him from the people before someone believed his nonsense about everyone being connected at the heart that beat in unison as one.

"The little girl feared for the safety of her mentor and herself if she became visible in her differences. Her mentor said, *Fear not, child. Man nor beast can harm the heart. One day in the far far future, your heart will be larger than your body and no one will ever be able to harm you because your heart protects you.*

"In time the people ignored her mentor and called him just a silly fool who sits on a hill with his wild imagination. But he always told her, *Remember one day you will have to speak of what's in your heart and not fear people saying, 'She is just a fool sitting on the hill. Pay no attention to her.' Live from your heart and you will wear the label, Fool on the Hill, as a badge of honor.*

"Many lifetimes passed. Each time she had wondered if she had the courage to become a 'fool on the hill.' Each time, she did not. Her heart collected more and more wisdom, more and more love, more and more courage. But not enough courage to override the fear of harm if she spoke her heart.

"Then came a life when her mentor was a maker of music, music of such intense creative energy, it exploded facade. The people ridiculed him because his music was different and unacceptable. They did not want their facade exploded. But he composed the music anyway, because it came from his heart. And she wanted to be that brave, but she was not.

"Her mentor continued to have many talks with her about the bravery required to open her heart for all. He always reminded her that harm could not come as long as one believed in their inner song, instead of what the majority demanded. He found great joy in being the Fool on the Hill. He knew that was among the greatest lives any could have. Oh, but to offer a meaning of life to the public, not caring if they responded by bombarding him with garbage. He knew who he was. He was—*The All.*

"Her heart continued to expand, accumulating wisdom, beauty, and love. One day she said, *This is all that my heart can hold in silence! I must emerge! I will leave early from this child's body. When I am reborn into my next body, I will share my heart with all and become the true Fool on the Hill.* It was a tearful departure, but the next life would be the one.

"In her and her mentor's next life, she was preparing to be born. She hesitated, fearing exploitation, ridicule, and harm. Her mentor's words rang across her awareness. *Be not afraid. No one can harm you if you believe in your heart.*

"She couldn't make up her mind if she would appear or not. Finally, she pushed past the fear and made her appearance. She birthed from her mother's womb with a mighty cry, *I don't want to be born! There will be too much pain!*

"She had arrived under the promise of her mentor's shield of protection. He held it tightly around her. But she was ever taunted by the awareness that he would gradually fade into the background so she could test her heart. This time it was she, who must not be crushed by words like, *Oh she is just a silly fool on a hill. Pay no attention to her nonsense.*

"As she grew, her mentor told her often, *For us to come into balance, you must reveal your heart and come forth in this world. I must retreat. This time the stage is yours. I'll help you build it. This time girl, we will do it.*

"She knew he had reached heights of wealth and power, and then gave it all up. He became a Fool on the Hill, but this time he didn't speak to the world as he usually did. This meant that it was her turn to take her place as the Fool on the Hill. She knew her heart would be put to the test, because it was this life that she had vowed not to hide.

"She wore a sign in her heart of plenty. The sign was etched in permanent ink. *Only the brave can open the heart fully and share that heart with all, no matter what.*

"One day when her time to emerge neared, she asked the Fool, *Tell me once more how to shield myself from people's cruel words and actions.*

"He said, *The words bounce off you when you know it is an honor to be called a silly Fool on the Hill.*

"She began to express her heart. Each time an arrow was shot in her direction, she said, *I feared I would be crushed, but here I am.*

"Her mentor would reply, *Dear child, you can't be crushed if you live inside the moment. The moment is the point of creation. The moment is the place where you are—the all of all, everyone, the fan and the critic. From there, you will see that the arrows shot at you are made of paper. They can't hurt you, unless you perceive them as steel tips dipped in poison-tongue-stories of re-peat, old old stories kept alive by fearing harm. Only you can harm your heart by not believing in yourself. You—the carrier of wisdom, you—who have apprenticed under a Fool on the Hill . . . alas, have become The Fool.*

"She continued to express. Sometimes she was loved. Some-times she was hated. Sometimes she wanted to run away and hide again. When she tried to hide, he was always there to say, *Go forth and ride the winds of change. Be the warrior. Let your sword be the wisdom of Creative Energy flowing up your spine on route to the heart. Channel the symphonies that are the vibration of to-tality. Then you will have the key to acquire permanent residence on the hill where fools reside. There, you will see beauty in all things, even the ugly. False fools, those that feign wisdom cannot trick you unless you become blind to who you are. Are you not be-coming the greatest Fool on the Hill ever?*

"She watched her Fool on the Hill as he began to retreat. And there he said to her his great goodbye. *You have been taught well. You have built a throne of Creative Energy with a heart of hearts. Then child, wear your title "Fool" with great honor. Live from the moment, from the point of creation, also known as Susan the Great, Susan the Brave. I will watch you from afar where I prepare for my next adventure of some new foolship not yet invented and yet waiting for me.*

"*Then dear child, be this old warrior's successor and shine bravely to all. To those who decry you as a fool, simply reply, 'Take your best shot. I care not who prints that signature on me. I wear it with esteem for the one who went before me. The one who spoke his words even though he can't spell them. He, who broke barriers recognizing the beauty in garbage as only a Fool on the Hill can. He who turned a key to find a moment, and dis-covered' The All.' It is I. It is I. It is I. Don't you know who I am?*"

I woke up sobbing. I could almost see my future. I almost had the confidence and the faith I needed. Almost. Smoke curled on the burned street. Liberty was draped over my stomach, asleep, or unconscious. I felt her beating heart. I felt mine. I had crossed over into something . . . in the dream. Had He come to tell me goodbye . . . in the dream? He seemed to believe in me . . . in the dream. In the dream, I seemed to have accomplished what I actually haven't. I still hadn't done the actual deed: use The Warrior, stand tall, and express my heart to the world.

I suddenly became aware of the hot stifling air binding me to old ways. I had to rise from the past, stand tall, and break free! I sat up, holding Liberty so she wouldn't fall.

She awakened and threw her arms around me. She said, "I had a dream. In the dream, all realities were born from the same place, a core of some kind."

"Libby, did He come to you in your dream and tell you this?"

She parted from me. "Yes, but would you call me Liberty?"

I nodded. "Yes, right, Liberty. Liberty, do you think what we dreamt is real?" I knew all dreams were real, but this one seemed too good to be true.

She nodded. "Yes." She rose and reached out her hand. "Let's walk." She smiled. Now she was the wise one, and I the student—she that was me. We can learn from ourselves.

I took her hand and rose.

We walked hurriedly under the boiling sky, over garbage and broken bricks and splintered two by fours, oil, gasoline, and blood. We walked past accident scenes, fireman and policemen every-where, stretchers and ambulances traveling every which way. Liberty led me out of the ruins toward the beckoning forest. "You must replenish," she declared, "and have courage to let your heart become larger than your body."

I gulped. "Why are you using those words Liberty? Why *those* words?"

She shrugged her shoulders. "They just came to me. Anyway, your old world is crashed. Time to rebuild. Be brave, Susan."

"Don't worry, Liberty. I will use My Warrior. I will."

We entered the forest, my little comrade and I. The trees welcomed us. Where was He—physically? I hoped He hadn't left me, not before I could receive the rainbow wand. Had I let Him down? Had I let me down? I didn't know. However, since the dream, I felt driven to find Him. But first, I needed to pay attention to my body. I was a physical mess and needed to tend myself. The old me would not have tended myself. Perhaps, there was hope for me yet.

We settled under a canopy of leafy sycamore. I leaned my back against the bark and pressed my hands over my growling stomach. I looked at my grimy bare feet, cut and blistered. I rubbed the sole of my foot against fallen sycamore leaves and soft dirt. My feet could know comfort, not just pain. Home sweet home. So much more than the House of Cards.

Liberty sat facing me, crossed-legged, dirt clumps tangled in the strands of her messy pigtails. She didn't seem to care.

My tattered clothes were barely on me, just rags and flaps of dirty cloth hanging down. The cool shade crept into my hot bones. Though inspired, I was weary, so weary.

Liberty leaned in. "Where is He, do you think?"

I wiped the sweat off my forehead. "Maybe Highway Eleven, Oh, I hope not, not yet. I did not say goodbye."

"Well, what exactly is this Highway Eleven?"

I closed my eyes contemplating Highway Eleven, and my fear that maybe I'd lost Him to it. How could I continue without Him? After knowing such quintessential brilliance of realities beyond the mundane, depression would consume me if I did not keep going, in a sense, toward the light, toward illumination. Could I do it without Him? I had to emerge in the world as a whole human being, warrior inclusive. I *had to* make it happen.

Liberty cleared her throat. "Well? Are you going to tell me about Highway Eleven?"

I said, "I will explain it the best I can, although I don't think I have the whole picture, and it is my understanding that the whole picture is nearly if not completely impossible to perceive from a human standpoint. Anyway, it's something like this: We come into the vibration of the Great Earth Story through Highway Eleven. Once finished experiencing earth through many life cycles in the perception of time, we also exit through Highway Eleven."

I told her everything I knew, everything He told me, and even things He didn't. I yearned to search for Him, but then I knew even He would want Liberty and I to rejuvenate. We bathed in a stream, combed each other's hair, and gathered feasts of fruit, nuts, and tubers in the radiant forest that opened itself as our refuge. Our retreat was nourishing, but my heart began growing heavy. Time to resolve what I feared most. One always knows this when anxiety rises from being stationary.

Time to find Him, if I wasn't too late. I closed my eyes and went into deep meditation. I sensed He'd not yet departed, yet He was fading rapidly. Even if I could find Him, could I restore His confidence in me? Could I restore *my* confidence in me? Perhaps His unfinished business with me is what held Him here.

Liberty and I set out on a grueling fruitless search for Him. We searched many days and nights, in dreams and other alternate realities, like a search for the Holy Grail. Weariness consumed us.

One great night, we heard His signal, like sonar indicating His location. Oh, this was it, this was the day. The day He left us. The day that changed me forever.

The black night yielded no moon, no stars, no guiding light. Liberty slept on my back as I hiked toward the sonar sound. I stumbled in the dark, catching myself just before I fell. Time was running short, but time was not up. I didn't fall. Not really, not in life, not from Him, not even from myself. I just hadn't climbed far enough or fast enough. But now I would. Now, I must.

I followed His call into dawn and all the next day, until dusk. My muscles ached. My search for Him was not the cause. The search for myself had taken a cumulative toll on this loyal body.

The signal had stopped. I saw Him nowhere. I looked south to Mud Lake, southeast to the House of Cards, east to the Desert of Loneliness, southwest to the Cave of Wounds and west to The Minefield, northwest to the Tunnel of Confrontation, and north to the Quakes that cracked my old world. I glimpsed the State Line, but I'd never go back there. I knew for certain, He wouldn't.

What now? What more could I do? I had given everything. I tried my best. I rolled Liberty gently off my back and laid her to rest upon soft desert sand by a mesquite tree.

The sun was setting in orange and lavender. The darkening sky shadowed a lonely distant mountain. I dropped to the sand in despair, hunched over, face to the ground, and sobbed. My tears sank into the earth. I wished them to fall through the earth to the place where Ancient Ones in wisdom dwell. "Oh Ancient Ones!" I cried. "Arise in me!" And even though I was calling to the Ancient Ones, an old comfortable belief I had, I knew I was really calling to Creative Energy where all beliefs are born.

I began breathing heavily. My head burned. "Let me see Him one more time!" And even though I was praying to something I deemed greater than myself, I knew it was to myself I prayed. I began to sweat and pant. The flame of creation consumed me.

"There you are." His whimsical, ancient, innocent, beautiful voice settled in my ears like healing music.

I lifted my head. The heat in my face cooled like lava turning to land. He was before me, almost invisible, My Fool. A bright comet tail stretched behind Him.

He said, "It's time to say goodbye. Time for this old warrior to move on."

I rose. My knees cracked, expelling pockets of pain I'd held for centuries. The darkening desert skies had turned purple, and His silhouette was the fondest, dearest shape of anything I'd ever seen in my life. His bright eyes were more vibrant than mundane eyes could ever be. His gazed locked into mine so deeply, I thought my soul would disintegrate.

He removed His Walkman and attached it to the ragged waist of my jeans, and placed the headphones on my ears. Mahler's 9th Symphony played lightly with sweeping tones of exquisite gentleness—the vibration of which He had earlier claimed would be, for Him, His exit music. He said, "I give you the music machine that has touched me so. Remember, the music is always playing, but the headphones remind you to listen."

I nodded in appreciation. "Thank you." My eyes watered. "I've been searching for you."

His voice came clear even with music in my ears. "I could only be found in depths you'd not yet traversed. I could not leave this state of being to come to you, lest I fall from it. But alas, you have come far enough for me to see you one last time. As my mundane self goes to sleep in the western skies, unearthly memories move in to occupy the void. It is as if the sun holds the story and when it sets, boundaries widen. References lose their power, the face of reality loses focus, and the sun follows the story over the hill and out of sight. Without identity, attunement comes calling, for that which is and that which is not. Facelessness is within reach now as the sun goes to sleep and the great desert comes to life. From moment to moment, the newness is difficult to hold, but easier as the night skies fall into place."

I said, "I . . . I am so glad I found you."

His full toned voice dropped like a heavy stone into the pools of my quintessence. "Open that final gate in you. Hold your sword high and champion your need to express. Expose your inner glow to this world, unafraid, because you feel the pulse of all worlds. Your dreams awaken. You begin now to remember the beginning of all things."

With ears open and clear, I listened.

"I have walked you through the inner worlds that I have known. I have given you all the gems of this Old Fool's wisdom. You can now dance in the core of the symphony that turns you inside out to fulfill *your* intent."

My forehead tightened. "I don't want you to leave."

"Turn around, Susan."

"Why? You also told me to turn around when my world was falling apart. Why?"

"Turn around."

I was afraid if I turned around, I'd see My Warrior mad at me for not using him, or The Nun, or some sick character in my psyche. I took a deep breath and turned slowly around. There before me, was an apparition, a woman of fluid prism energy. She said to me. "I am the Goddess Susannah, your wise and ancient self."

I gasped, warmed by her powerful presence.

She touched my shoulder ever so lightly. "Come unto me, for I am you. Release your Fool, and feel Him rise inside you, for He is you, and you are I, and I am Him. Indeed, we are all each other. Surrender your small self to the large self—that is me. The *me that is you*, always here, always ready to fill your need, if only you will allow."

I heard His voice behind me. "Choose."

"Yes," I said on quivering breath, "I surrender the limited me to the limitless me." I moved inside her and I felt her move inside me, and everything changed. Liberty moved into my heart with cooing joy. My Warrior rose up, tall and mighty within me, metaphorical sword raised high. I felt other aspects of myself emerge and blend. My insides crackled and warmed. Safe. I felt safe. I was larger somehow, stronger someway, charged with a knowing that defied intellect, and love that surpassed need.

I turned back around to My Fool, My Beloved Fool. "You are going to leave earth now, aren't you?"

"There is no leaving or arrival, not really. Everything is already said and done, and everything always is and always was, outside of time and space in Creative Energy."

"Even so, will I, Susan, ever see *you* again?"

"Identities defocus from the physical world. Some call it death. However, there is a marker in our brains that when activated can sense the deceased in this location and time. Some call it talking to the dead."

"You mean, you will still be here?"

"Here, there, and everywhere."

"What?"

"You can contact the me you have known, even though I may have slipped into other identities in other worlds, or taken flight into unexplored realms."

"You mean, I can still talk to you?"

"You will find me in the Wall of Remembrance. And you might find me elsewhere if you hone your skills in otherworldly travel. Or, I might visit you in some way while simultaneously living out other rays of experiences—just as you are now, though you don't remember or are not aware. To someone else, you are dying. To another, you are being born. We have all just recently died."

My throat knotted. "We have all just recently died. We die over and over in so many ways, and are likewise ever being born: cells always decaying and replenishing, thoughts coming and going, everything always in change, and yet constant.

I smiled at Him, almost wisely. "From this moment forth, I will see with polyphonic eyes."

He nodded lightly with a satisfying grin. "I have danced with your being through perceived millenniums in this earth adventure. Our intent with each other is complete." Fluid glossed His eyes. "This Old Fool will miss your innocent face, your wisdom-hungry mind, your gentle touch . . . ." He reached His fingers toward me, but stepped back. "And now I go where no words exist. I go where the symphony lives before it turns into music . . . I go—I."

Dark shadows inside me fell away. I embraced my humanity, the human struggle, and the sweet streams of beauty that flow through all. I bowed to Him, tears stinging my eyes.

My Fool walked backward into His own brilliant trail of light, "It is I. It is I. It is I. Don't you know who I am?" His hand stretched toward me as if to touch me for the last time.

I stretched my hand toward Him, reaching, reaching to touch My Fool. But we would not touch. It was too late, or maybe too early.

I tried to walk forward, but an invisible wall blocked me. He vanished in the light. In the outer world, His heart stopped beating.

I cupped my hands over my face, catching hot tears that stung my scraped cheeks . . . burning, itching, and flooding down my neck. I knew He wasn't really dead, only changing focus from one world to another.

The headphones He'd bequeathed me hugged my ears like a nanny. The end of Mahler's 9th symphony swelled in tribute to My

Fool. Gentle melodies entwined, bringing all vibrations together, surely melting all hearts into one . . . great . . . heart.

Still, my tears filled the vault of sorrow. I was Sorrow. No, not because He departed, but because it was not my time to go with Him. It was not my time. And I knew He'd always be with me in some way, and I with Him, for after all, there really is no 'I'—save Creative Energy. But, His human presence was gone. Gone. Anyway, I loved that man: the contours of His face, His way, His calming and sometimes disturbing presence that ever led me deeper into myself. My Fool . . . oh, My Fool was gone! His body was empty, but I mustn't cling to it. I mustn't.

My tears came hard. Grief pounded in my chest even though I knew He was freed into something beautiful. My cheeks stung, saturated in liquid salt. And I felt the salt of my life, and what it would be like without Him. Then, I suddenly remembered that I had forgotten to ask Him about other worldly beings, and transitions from one world to the next. I . . . I forgot to ask Him why there were holes in toes of His shoes! But no, I mustn't think like this. He said we feel best when we release everything to our own grand design, and believe in it—believe in ourselves.

Maybe releasing each other was our greatest accomplishment. Maybe one day we'd be together in a new way, in a New World, in a reality that transcended earthly perspective. Or, what was I saying. We are all the same being. Separation is an illusion, a wonderful illusion that sparks creativity.

I gazed at the brilliant heavens, and thought of the galaxies beneath our planet, just as divine as those above. I realized for the first time how small and large I was all at once. Somehow, some way, He would always know me. My heart was a giant. I had been undone. I was no longer a clone of someone's dream, a creation of the collective mind. I was hope, love, and promise. I was a time capsule and a composition waiting to be played. I was a majestic explosion that would imprint upon seeking minds the ecstasy of living and the boundless expanse of room to become.

The palm of my hand warmed, almost hot, flooding energy, condensing . . . condensing. I lifted my hand and looked. The rainbow wand! I had received it. I actually had! In the woe of my *un*becoming, I had been reborn. My clothes had dissolved. I was naked in the glow of my aura that had become a rainbow of colors, shining all the gems of wisdom that I'd internalized.

Then, who was I? I didn't know. But I didn't disappear. I became more visible, using my favorite word—no. No to the old ways, the old stories, the old choices that I had at long last transcended. A tone rose from my breath into the physical world, a flood to some, a trickle to many, filling the dark corners of unawareness. The tone resonated past facades into the chaotic and the staled, into the ailing and the seekers. And I was not a martyr. I was just singing my polyphonic eleven gem song. I knew it then that the rainbow wand was all gems in one. And I held that wand like a sword, guarding my right to shine—My Warrior integrated at last.

I hear My Fool talking to me now and then from places of existence I have yet to visit. "Then do that. It is the way it is supposed to be. Walk the Winds. Live with gusto. Change the past as if it never was. This day of days. This night of nights. This moment of moments. Ain't— life—great! And, it is I. It is I. It is I. Don't you know who I am?"

And what is the 'I' if not Pure Creative Energy.

His words echo through me in books and lectures, grocery stores and gas stations, "When intellect subsides and pain forces surrender to wholeness, when we no longer blame and take ownership, when the open mind soars in the overview: then and only then do we order the symphonies that take us to the gate of illumination with a combination to the lock; then and only then, do we experience the smallest spark of Pure Creative Energy; then and only then, do we take the first step of freedom on the road of awakening. Then, it starts."

Time for you to start too.

THE START

201

Breinigsville, PA USA
28 September 2010
246307BV00003B/97/P